EVALUATION
IN
MATHEMATICS

Twenty-Sixth Yearbook

THE NATIONAL COUNCIL OF TEACHERS
OF MATHEMATICS
Washington, D. C., 1961

Correspondence relating to and orders for
additional copies of the Twenty-Sixth
Yearbook and earlier yearbooks should be
addressed to:

THE NATIONAL COUNCIL OF TEACHERS
OF MATHEMATICS
1201 Sixteenth Street, N.W., Washington, D.C. 20036

Library of Congress Catalog Card Number: 61–11906

Manufactured in the United States of America

PREFACE

EVALUATION IN MATHEMATICS has been written to help teachers of mathematics—elementary, secondary, and junior college—to improve their techniques of evaluating achievement. We have attempted to apply basic principles of measurement to the evaluation of mathematics achievement from grade 1 through grade 14. We do not prescribe rigid procedures; we offer instead a wealth of ideas and illustrations from which the reader may select those applicable to his particular situation.

We hope this yearbook will be a useful reference for every mathematics teacher. It furnishes specific examples and general principles for building tests, revising report forms, and scheduling testing programs; it offers help in making good decisions when interpreting scores, evaluating curriculum, and instituting a program of ability grouping; it suggests criteria for consideration in making an inventory of current status, planning a research project in mathematics education, and selecting the objectives of mathematics instruction. This yearbook will be useful as a basic text and reference book in the preparation of new mathematics teachers, in in-service programs, and in graduate work for experienced teachers. It will be successful, however, only if it stimulates schools and teachers to institute improved and expanded evaluation programs in mathematics.

The members of the editorial committee express their thanks to the authors of the several chapters. A sincere word of appreciation is small recognition for the time, talent, and work each author has given his task. In addition, we extend our thanks to the many persons who have supplied materials and services for this production. In particular, we wish to express our thanks to Miriam Goldman of the NCTM Central Office for her excellent editorial work. For us the satisfaction of participating in the publication of this important information has been its own reward.

The Committee
Robert S. Fouch
E. Glenadine Gibb
Max A. Sobel
J. Fred Weaver
Donovan A. Johnson, *Chairman*

CONTENTS

Introduction

DONOVAN A. JOHNSON

THE EVALUATION of instruction has been called the quality control of the educational program. It is a means by which the quality of our mathematics programs can be constantly improved. Through evaluation activities we chart the present achievement of our students and measure the progress they have made in the desired direction.

The evaluation of the achievement of our students is an integral part of our teaching of mathematics. Evaluation is a time-consuming activity, frequently tedious; we must prepare test questions, score papers, record marks, and interpret scores. It is often discouraging, especially when we find out how little our students have apparently learned from our carefully planned instruction. But evaluation is an indispensable, recurring task which becomes increasingly more important when we commit ourselves to the ideal of having each of our pupils achieve the optimum of his potential. It is the purpose of this yearbook to help mathematics teachers build an evaluation program that can function effectively in the classroom.

Plan of the Yearbook

This yearbook emphasizes three important aspects in an effective evaluation program. First, there are the theoretical elements, involving the determination of objectives, content, method, and organization; the statistical procedure accepted for the treatment of test scores (summarization, translation into derived scores, and interpretation of results); and the technical qualities of the measuring instrument itself such as reliability, validity, and discriminatory power.

1

A second aspect of evaluation consists of such procedures as the writing of test items, recording and reporting of scores, and interpreting of specific scores; and such materials as published tests currently available.

The third aspect we emphasize is the establishment of a comprehensive evaluation program. Such a program should apply the theoretical and practical aspects of evaluation to a specific school situation.

The chapters of this yearbook present these aspects as follows:

1. The general theory of evaluation: Chapters 2, 3, and 4;
2. Practical techniques of evaluation for mathematics teachers: Chapters 5, 6, 7, 8, and 9;
3. Evaluation principles applied to classroom problems: Chapter 10.

The committee planning this yearbook made a detailed outline of each chapter before attempting to secure writers. Each writer was then asked to treat his suggested topics in any order or manner he considered appropriate. It was hoped that this plan would keep to a minimum duplication of material and gaps in the coverage. However, some duplication in the development of related topics seems necessary for the exposition. The material in each chapter reflects the point of view of its author.

Not all possible topics on evaluation will be found in this book. Diagnostic testing and daily quizzes, for example, are barely mentioned. This yearbook might have considered the evaluation of teaching effectiveness, of classroom facilities, of an entire curriculum. The committee, however, decided to limit the discussion to the evaluation of the *achievement* of the mathematics student.

There are times when it is difficult to separate evaluation and the teaching process. For example, although item analysis focuses on individual student weaknesses or strengths and the need for individualized instruction, the instruction aspect was not considered appropriate material for the yearbook. Likewise the problem of curriculum development was considered beyond the scope of this book.

With reference to statistical analysis, the committee felt that the elementary statistics needed for the computation of scores discussed in this book would be a part of every mathematics teacher's background.

The committee would have liked to include material on the appraisal of mental processes in the learning of mathematics. As teachers of mathematics, we are deeply concerned about developing skill in productive thinking. Too often, many of us find ourselves knowing little about the relations between the solutions given by our students and the thought processes that led to those solutions. However, tests for appraising higher mental processes such as concept formation, problem solving, and creative thinking in mathematics do not exist. Although several types of instruments are being developed in connection with research projects in this field, these check lists, rating scales, and observation methods are not now sufficiently developed to be of much use to the classroom teacher. Hence, this yearbook does not include a discussion of or examples of this type of appraisal.

Brief Synopsis of the Yearbook

General Theory

In Chapter 2 Sueltz discusses the many roles of evaluation in the mathematics classroom. One of the most important of these is the improvement of our instruction. Through evaluation we will be able to determine the effectiveness of the techniques, materials, and content of our teaching. Thus evaluation gives us a basis for building the curriculum and selecting methods of teaching that will develop the desired mathematical competence. Evaluation has potential value for improving the progress of individual students. We need to determine readiness for instruction, to diagnose weaknesses and strengths, to locate difficulties or superior mental capacities. Instruction may then be planned to meet the needs of individual students.

Evaluation activities in themselves may also be of value to the pupil participating in them. Competition with one's own record, the class record, or national norms can be a stimulating experience. Completing a test is an intense learning experience in itself. The process of discussing a test and correcting errors helps locate areas of misunderstanding and wrong procedures, and it reinforces correct learning.

In Chapter 3 Hartung discusses basic principles of evaluation of mathematics achievement. Here the emphasis is on measurement in terms of the objectives of mathematics instruction, and we must, of course, be clear as to what our objectives are. When we know what kind of behavior indicates the attainment of our objectives, we can measure our progress. Usually we measure the progress or growth of our students in building computational skills or in memorizing facts and rules. It is equally important, and usually more difficult, to measure understandings, attitudes, problem-solving ability, and logical-reasoning capacity. Our instruments for this purpose must be valid, relevant, and reliable. Then when scores are obtained, we must interpret the record properly before deciding what action to take.

Merwin tells us in Chapter 4 about specific procedures for the construction of achievement tests and for the analysis of test results—converting raw scores to ranks, standard scores, or norms. Test items should be written so that the student response indicates the degree of attainment of a specific objective. Then results must be analyzed for information about the performance of the class, the performance of individual students, and the test itself. This information is used to improve instruction by the teacher, learning by the student, and the measurement made by the instrument.

Practical Techniques

In Chapter 5 Sobel and Johnson apply the principles of test construction to the writing of various types of test items. Different items are presented to show different ways an idea or objective may be tested. The analysis of these items shows the kind of information we get from responses to them. This chapter contains items from reading tests, performance tests, problem-solving tests, tests of creativeness and visualization, and tests of logical reasoning, as well as achievement tests. However, the chapter does not attempt to be a storehouse of items that measure all objectives. Instead, it shows possibilities for improved evaluation resulting from careful construction and judicious use of test items.

In Chapter 6 Myers presents a description of available published evaluation materials. This chapter will be helpful in the selection of tests that are uniquely suited to the local mathematics program. It presents criteria and techniques for the selection of tests. Some emphasize the manipulative aspects of mathematics, and others emphasize interpretive items of applications of mathematics. Some of them can be used to measure year-to-year progress in mathematics, while others measure achievement in specific topics. Published tests usually furnish norms such as grade equivalents or percentile ranks or standard scores. Myers has supplemented his chapter with an annotated bibliography, which appears in the appendix, of recent prognostic tests, diagnostic tests, unit tests, and long-range achievement tests. Because so many things are happening so fast in mathematics today, this bibliography will soon be out-of-date. The committee feels, however, that it will be extremely helpful to the mathematics teacher to have this information available now. Since the mathematics curriculum is undergoing extensive revision, the selection of appropriate evaluation instruments is becoming both more difficult and more important than ever. There is also an urgent need for new tests that are in harmony with the objectives of new curricula.

The evaluation of attitudes and appreciations, an exciting field of new developments, is discussed by Corcoran and Gibb in Chapter 7. Student behavior that illustrates attitudes, appreciations, and curiosities needs to be evaluated by special appraisal instruments. These include such devices as questionnaires, check lists, rating scales, interviews, and diaries. Although the reliability and validity of current appraisal instruments in this field are in doubt, much progress is being made in developing usable techniques and devices. This chapter opens new vistas in evaluation for every mathematics teacher.

In Chapter 8 Kalin presents examples of specific evaluation procedures sampled from within actual school testing programs in selected schools. The specific procedures described illustrate the theoretical principles of earlier chapters in actual practice. These examples show how schools are using evaluation for grouping, acceleration, and guidance. The examples also describe test selection, test construction, and the use of test scores. They show us the great potential of a carefully planned evaluation program for the improvement of instruction, guidance, curriculum, and research activities of mathematics teachers.

After achievement has been measured, we need to consider the ways of recording, interpreting, and reporting the scores, as discussed by Kellogg in Chapter 9. Records must be made that are readily available to the teacher, parent, counselor, or administrator. Sometimes scores must be converted to standard scores, grade equivalents, or percentile ranks. These scores are usually based on norms which can be very useful if interpreted intelligently in terms of the sample on which the norms are based. To be "up" to the norm also means to be "down" to the norm. The norms may be unsatisfactory as a standard or measure of our class because our class may be different in aptitude from the norm sample.

Chapter 9 also includes unique sample report forms and record forms and gives criteria for building a suitable mathematics report, emphasizing the proper interpretation of a score or mark so that the record will correctly communicate evaluation information.

Applications

Chapter 10 is an overview in which Fouch describes evaluation principles in action, taking into account many of the day-to-day problems of the mathematics teacher. This chapter presents a variety of suggestions about how to collect evaluation information, how to interpret it, and how to use it effectively. The practical interpretations of this chapter, which emphasizes many important ideas of previous chapters, will give the teacher many tips for improving his evaluation techniques.

Summary

Evaluation in the mathematics classroom, a technical task for which we need adequate materials and technical information, is a highly satisfying experience for the learner and the teacher when it is accomplished in an accurate and comprehensive manner. The yearbook committee has attempted to present material that the mathematics teacher can immediately translate into classroom activities. We have tried to cover a wide range of instruction in mathematics from grade 1 through grade 14. We have collected examples of specific programs, sample items, and report forms that teachers have found successful in the mathematics classroom. We have included instructions for the preparation of evaluation materials as well as for the interpretation of the results obtained. But this yearbook will be successful only if it stimulates the teacher to plan an improved evaluation program, to prepare new and better tests, to use the published resources, and to use available evaluation information to improve his instruction.

The Role of Evaluation
In the Classroom

BEN A. SUELTZ

E VALUATION, an essential part of the mathematics program at every level, should be the handmaiden of instruction and learning. It is not a separate entity in a good school program. It may serve to improve the instructional program in the school, to enhance the effectiveness of the teacher, to aid the student in learning mathematics, and to furnish valid data for research. Levels of evaluation may range from testing for simple factual knowledge such as "12 in. = 1 ft." to testing for more sophisticated abilities such as abstracting the mathematics from a complex structure and expressing the inherent mathematical relationships. The latter involves analysis and insight at a very high level. Satisfactory evaluation beyond the lowest levels requires specialized understanding and skill.

This chapter is concerned with the many services good evaluative procedures may provide to enhance the learning of mathematics. Our concept of the role of evaluation is necessarily determined by our vision of the field of mathematics and the values to be gained from study in this field. We may teach in terms of facts to be memorized without understanding and appreciation; this yearbook, however, views mathematics as much more than a collection of facts and skills.

Mathematics is an elegant field of human creation. It is concerned with ideas of quantity and structure, with patterns, and relationships. In the study of mathematics a student must learn facts, develop concepts, use symbols, and master processes and procedures. But he should also learn to develop generalizations and to sense the presence

7

of mathematical ideas and structures not only in abstract situations but also in many areas of human activity. He should develop his reasoning powers in order to prove or disprove a statement by deduction or to predict an event with appropriate probability. It is the function of evaluation to determine how well a student has mastered these varied aspects of mathematics.

Determining Levels of Learning

Mathematics is an important part of the curriculum at all school levels, beginning in the kindergarten. It is organized in a sequence of topics and activities that are associated with appropriate levels of maturity and ability of the students. Evaluation can identify and define steps and levels in the sequence that are appropriate for a given grade or age level. Careful evaluation should show not only how far a pupil has progressed in the major steps of a sequence, but also how well he has understood and mastered a particular step. Good evaluation will show the facts and skills mastered (and those not mastered) by the student, his attitude toward the subject, and the depth of understanding and insight accompanying his work.

Consider the way young children think of *eight*. To one child it may be only a symbol "8" which he has learned to write and which he calls by name singly and in sequence with other symbols. To another, various elements of "eightness" enter; he senses that the concept of eight involves the collection idea, and that 8 may be subgrouped into 4 and 4, 3 and 5, and so on. And from these subgroupings he begins to establish addition and subtraction combinations and the first notions of division (sharing and separating) and of multiplication (2 groups of 4). Also, eight may be related to other numbers in the form "1 more than 7" or "2 less than 10"; these ideas are later used in column addition and in thinking with number scales. Still later he distinguishes between the numeral "8" and the number 8. Some children soon grasp the idea of one-to-one correspondence and have a very good generalization of eight. At a more mature level they distinguish between 8 as a counting number, a rational number, and a real number. Thus it is apparent that with a primary concept such as *eight* there are levels of learning that can be identified and evaluated.

It is comparatively easy to determine whether or not a student can add, solve a specific type of problem, or use a table of logarithms, and to place him at an appropriate step in his sequence of learning mathematics. To determine the level of sophistication at which he works and his depth of understanding of a major topic, however, requires a much more refined procedure. Levels of understanding are associated with structures of mathematical relationships. The boy who senses that 6 × 7½ produces the same result as 3 × 15 and chooses the latter to perform the multiplication has a higher level of insight into relationships than the one who doggedly performs the former. Similarly, the one who notes that "65,800 bricks at $78.50" is the same basic pattern as "4 pencils at 7¢ each" has reached a comparatively high level of generalization.

A still higher level is reached when the multiplication process is generalized as $ab = c$. A test of understanding must differentiate among such levels as recognizing a special case of a general principle, stating the principle in words, stating the principle in symbols, applying the principle to a new problem, and using the principle to develop a new concept through a long chain of reasoning. Teachers of mathematics must be concerned with the identification and evaluation of these levels of learning; they must be concerned also with the problem of helping a student reach a higher level. The task is complicated because each pupil learns as an individual.

Evaluation is useful in determining the relative ease or difficulty of learning, applying, or remembering a topic, and it serves as a guide in scaling and arranging curriculum materials. We need to know how long it takes to master a given concept, the suitable concepts for different grades, the appropriate sequence of concepts, and the aids the teacher needs to build mastery of each concept.

New Developments in Mathematics

Evaluation of the instructional program in mathematics has become more important because of these recent developments and pressures:

New mathematics curricula are being advocated and tested by experimentation and research.

New mathematics content is available and is being proposed for inclusion at several levels of instruction.

New devices and materials of instruction are being developed and promoted by financial resources never before available to our schools.

New principles of learning are being emphasized in the presentation of mathematical concepts.

Society is demanding greater mathematical competence of all citizens than ever before.

National survival may depend upon the development of new mathematical concepts.

Traditional vs. New Curricula

Decisions must be made regarding the most effective instructional program. Certainly it is possible to evaluate the learning derived from a new curriculum, but is more difficult to determine whether new mathematical content is superior to more traditional content. In either case one may evaluate in terms of the objectives and goals, and one must make value judgments in terms of the data available.

While student enthusiasm toward a certain content may be appraised, its value as a criterion for selection of curriculum is uncertain. To illustrate, the basic concept of *sets* was taught to one group of students. They learned readily and enthusiastically, and they applied this concept as a unifying theme to their work with common and decimal fractions and percentage. When later they were expected to become as proficient as their traditional colleagues in computations and problems based upon percentage, their enthusiasm waned rapidly, and they did not do as well as the group of students in the traditional program. The conclusion one draws depends upon his values and objectives in mathematics. It is possible that the students involved with sets have a better basic understanding, will have greater residual knowledge ten years hence, and will have a finer appreciation of the nature of mathematics than their traditional colleagues. These outcomes may be as important as or more important than computational skills. Here evaluation must be subjected to value judgments.

Learning Materials

Materials for learning mathematics should also be evaluated. Is textbook *A* better than textbook *B* as a tool for learning algebra? Is a device based upon the linear concept of number better than one based upon the idea of a group or collection? Or can the one supplement the other? Is a manual-manipulative device better than a film or filmstrip for showing the change in a trigonometric function as an angle changes? Does a pupil respond better to one than to another device? Can we identify the pupil who is bored with and doesn't need a visual aid? Because many factors enter into a learning situation, it may be difficult to make an objective evaluation of materials of instruction in terms of their effectiveness with students. However, every time a book or device or film is used with a class, a prejudgment has been made. Continued use should require a careful appraisal in terms of the contribution the item has made to the mathematics program.

When an instructional program in mathematics is evaluated, the principles of learning employed by teachers and students should be identified and evaluated. Psychologists are now engaged in a variety of experiments in learning; the results of these experiments should be studied and considered for application to mathematics. Will electronic and mechanical boxes and devices replace much of the work now done by teachers? Can learning be individualized by one of these machines? Can discovery and the development of understanding and insight be fostered with them? For which phases of the mathematics program is it advantageous to employ a machine? Such questions can be answered only through proper modes of evaluation.

People involved with construction of a new mathematics curriculum frequently pool their own experiences and seek the advice of other teachers in choosing materials, selecting a sequence of topics, and placing these topics with respect to age or grade levels. These people are evaluating experience as they make decisions. But evaluation as to choice, arrangement, and placement of topics can and should be on a more scientific basis. Too often, one who is not experimentally oriented assumes that a novel development is unwise and/or impossible. Curriculum development should make increased use of carefully planned evaluation.

Curriculum Effectiveness

Perhaps the final test of a curriculum is its effectiveness as a framework to foster learning. How well do students progress toward the accepted goal? Are students able to apply their knowledge and skill in new situations? Is the content worthwhile and important mathematics? Does the content improve the student's ability to solve a problem for which he is not specifically trained? Does the content stimulate students to continue in mathematics courses? Are the topics and goals of suitable difficulty for the students who are expected to learn? Is the curriculum teachable and learnable?

Evaluation should be concerned with the improvement of instruction. Certainly some methods of teaching and guiding learning are superior to others and must be identified and evaluated. What factors seem to be determinants? How much learning can be expected of students at a given age or grade level? What methods are suitable for encouraging creativity and original thinking? Many questions concerning instruction can be answered by means of good evaluation procedures. Many other questions that cannot be answered readily by testing and formal evaluation are now being attacked by such other procedures as observation and interview and the study of the thought processes of individual students.

The Role of Mathematics in Our Civilization

The casual citizen today has some appreciation of mathematics and its importance in business, industry, and new scientific developments. Individuals planning school programs, however, must know a great deal about the importance of mathematics in our society. What is the place of mathematics in the life of the citizen who is not technically employed? What would it be if this person acted intelligently in terms of mathematical concepts? For example, Mrs. A is satisfied with the 3 percent interest she receives on her savings, but Mr. B receives 4 percent with equal safety. And when Mr. B buys oranges by actual measurement, he receives 62 percent more for his money than Mrs. A, who buys by the dozen. It would not occur to Mrs. A that 4 percent is $33\frac{1}{3}$ percent better than 3 percent, or that the 62 percent saved by judicious purchases is compounded many times each year. This illustrates the bread-and-butter role of mathematics. But there are other roles of mathematics for the general citizen—the cultural and aesthetic, for example. An area of aesthetic satisfaction exists in mathematics as an elegant field of knowledge and mathematics as a structural medium in art, music, and drama. The general citizen would also find it worthwhile to know and appreciate the mathematical contributions associated with such names as Newton, Gauss, Descartes, Einstein, and Euclid.

It is not enough to appraise and evaluate historical contributions of mathematics to the progress of society. We must make value judgments in terms of the importance of such knowledge to our students and the amount of information about and appreciation of such contributions they should have. In these terms, is the mathematics now taught the best mathematics to equip the general citizen for his role in society?

Relation to Other Studies

The nature and contribution of mathematics must be evaluated not only as a separate entity but also in relation to other areas of study. For example, mathematics frequently serves as an organizing factor: the time line (number system) in history and the equation ($HCl + NaOH \rightarrow NaCl + H_2O$) in chemistry. In geography and the physical and biological sciences mathematics makes description specific and furnishes statistical values that are useful in interpretation and comparison. In the arts such mathematical concepts as symmetry, sequence, and proportion provide a convenient construct. The whole structure of music is noted mathematically. The farmer who discovers a curvilinear relationship between the amount of fertilizer and the harvest, and uses this in a crude way is doing essentially the same thing as the statistician or engineer who studies data and predicts a future performance by a more refined method of curve-fitting.

To present the role of mathematics in the development of our civilization we must evaluate the kinds of mathematical thinking and processes that are employed and determine the extent to which these should become a part of school work at the different levels.

Evaluations Made by Non-teachers

Mathematics programs are often criticized (evaluated) by people not directly engaged in their development or in the teaching of mathematics. Scholars, business tycoons, government officials, members of boards of education, school officers, and the general public freely express opinions which are their own evaluations of school mathematics programs. Frequently these evaluations are made with insufficient understanding of the nature of mathematics, the goals of instruction, and the learning process. School officials and mathematics teachers must evaluate such critical statements and interpret the mathematics program to the community. This requires a good understanding of mathematics and a thorough acquaintance with the local program—its aims, content, and procedures. It also requires information based on evaluation which shows the current status of the school program and progress that has been made. If critical statements are fair and they encourage a school to reappraise and defend its program, the net result should be wholesome. But it is the responsibility of the mathematics staff to exert leadership to insure that only people who are competent to evaluate a mathematics program do so. When school officials have had the intellectual courage to explain a new program, they have usually found the public eager to share in the responsibility for its success by furnishing the necessary financial resources as well as moral support. At one PTA meeting each parent received a copy of the standardized test given the children together with a profile of his child's score; this resulted in increased understanding and appreciation of the school program.

Evaluation and Research

The mathematics curriculum is currently in a ferment. Conflicting claims are made for traditional and newer mathematics at the elementary, the secondary, and the college levels. Decisions must be made about the topics included, the sequence of topics, and the immediate and remote goals of mathematics instruction. If these are to be wise decisions they must be based on experimentation and research. This calls for careful evaluation to furnish the information upon which final decisions may be based. Data collected in the evaluation of programs, of students' learning, and of the results of teaching procedures are the basis for educational research. Thus a school must evaluate as validly as possible and must keep good records, which should be available when needed.

Research is like a chain in that the end product can be no stronger than the weakest link. Frequently researchers fail to identify the weak links in data and too many tend to consider a number absolute when a probable error should be attached to it. The evaluator, then, must seek valid evaluations and form conclusions that are in harmony with the data. For example, even if no significant differences are found on traditional tests between students taking new courses and those taking standard courses, such other factors as interest and methods of thinking may be significantly different, though not measurable at this time.

Research can answer many questions, but it must be carried out by people who are competent to conduct such studies and to draw conclusions supported by the data. Consider a comparison of mathematics achievement in England with that in the United States. It was found of two carefully equated groups that the English students had a higher mean score than the American group. What conclusion may be drawn? Can inferences be made regarding mathematics programs in the two countries without more information?

Evaluation in Reporting Pupil Progress

Evaluation provides valuable data that is used in reporting to parents, in advising on school programs, and in studying many aspects of curriculum and school procedures. It provides the written record of a student's work in school, which may proceed with the student when he moves to another school. Frequently employers ask for the record, and they may request even the elementary school record. Again, it is most important that evaluations be valid and adequate and that the records be carefully preserved.

Occasionally one hears from a citizen that the schools today are not as good as they were a generation ago. Several schools have answered the question by producing a mathematics test of 25 years ago along with the records of the students at that time; they have given this same test to current groups of students of equal ability. As a result, valid information has been available for appraising local situations.

Effect of Evaluation on the Mathematics Student

The program, facilities, and instruction in a school should be designed for optimum intellectual growth and development of the student. How can evaluation most effectively promote this progress?

Measurement can determine a great deal about the student's mental ability, his likes and dislikes, his social development, his emotional maturity, his determination, his health, and his background of experience and learning at a particular school level. This information has an immediate bearing upon his potential success in a given area of mathematics. The importance of mental maturity and aptitude to learning in a sequential field such as mathematics must be considered. One would not teach the solution of oblique triangles at a level of maturity that cannot master necessary prelearning in arithmetic, algebra, and geometry. A first obligation is to guide the student into study for which he is ready in terms of mental maturity, aptitude and background of experience and learning. In addition, it is desirable that he have an interest in and a desire to learn mathematics. All students will not want to study advanced mathematics, and many probably should not study this subject beyond a minimal level.

Appropriate Placement

In many schools various tracks of study are available so that a student may be placed in a course suitable to his interest and aptitude. A student who is properly placed will be less likely to drop the study of mathematics before he has achieved his potential.

Placement in an appropriate course should be based on many evaluations such as achievement test scores, aptitude test scores, achievement records, and teacher judgment. Student attitudes are also important with regard to potential success in a given mathematics course. The educational climate of a school and of a community may be a positive or negative factor in encouraging pupils to continue the study of mathematics and in giving them the desire to succeed. The educational climate of a school includes such factors as the personality of the teachers, the arrangement and decor of rooms, and the intellectual atmosphere of the school and community. All these factors—placement in a course, experience, previous learning, will to succeed, and school atmosphere—affect a student and can be identified, defined, and evaluated.

At any stage in a mathematical sequence one should be able to appraise the achievement level of a student. This appraisal ideally includes many aspects of learning in addition to acquisition of facts and skills. It includes the student's attitude toward the work; the nature of his curiosity about and ingenuity with mathematics; his work habits and his methods of recording steps toward a conclusion; his ability to think, to exclude extraneous data, and to formulate a tentative procedure; his techniques and operations; and finally, his feeling of security with his answer or conclusion. The student should know not only that he is succeeding or failing but also in what respect he is so doing. Other chapters of this yearbook describe many procedures and devices for evaluating the factors we have discussed. A good appraisal and evaluation of a student's work will involve several procedures, and even the most objective procedure or instrument must be viewed as limited. The good teacher must be trained in evaluation so that he can and will make value judgments, and he must be given the best available materials with which to make these judgments.

Motivation

A student's motivation toward learning mathematics is an important factor which can be appraised and evaluated. Of course evaluation must first identify the level or type of motivation and then enhance and augment it with an aim toward improved learning. There may be many intertwined elements and factors in motivation, or there may be a single factor. What motivates Harry may not motivate his brother. The one may need to be convinced that it is necessary for him to learn mathematics; the other may be content and even thrilled with learning for its own sake and may find mathematical learning particularly appealing. Identifying the factors of motivation is probably more worthwhile than attempting to place the amount of motivation on a scale. A good teacher will seek to appraise the effectiveness of various devices that he uses for motivation. When is it desirable to use merited praise? When should he put the thumb down? When will he refer to honor and pride? Artistry in teaching means, in part, knowing when, how, and for whom various procedures are best applied. A teacher must constantly be evaluating his own procedures if he is to be most effective in guiding the learning of his students.

Evaluation can help answer such questions as the following: How much mathematics can various types of students learn? How much should they learn? What areas of study are most valuable to various types and levels of pupils? At what age can the gifted be identified and what might be done with them? How can a teacher best instruct for transfer at various levels?

Evaluating the Modes of Learning

One of the major objectives of instruction in mathematics is the development of mathematical insight and power. Two students may have the same native ability in mathematics, but one may have learned to explore and to think and to derive conclusions while the other may have achieved a high performance through rote memorization. The first possesses a mode or quality of learning which is considered much more valuable than the second. Many teachers believe that the mode of learning in mathematics is as important as the content, because a pattern of learning that features inquiry and thinking is extendible by the student and probably has transfer values far beyond a pattern of memorization. The teacher who permits an able student to succeed in his class by memorization with a minimum of thinking is doing a disservice to that student. Thus the teacher must constantly be evaluating the modes of learning employed by students, and the wise teacher will seek to nurture the elements of inquiry, discovery, understanding, and insight.

Experimentation

Most good teachers are willing to experiment with modes of learning and procedures exhibited in textbooks. Should long division be broken into seven steps or should the whole process be developed as a unit? Should the solution of linear equations be handled as four main types with several sub-steps or should the solution by axioms of algebra be a single large development? In answering such questions the teacher will be evaluating various approaches and may come to the conclusion that one method seems best for certain types of students while another serves other students better.

In guiding learning there is constant need to evaluate students in terms of their individual weaknesses and to seek modes of overcoming these weaknesses. Likewise, an experienced teacher has learned to recognize the normal hard spots in mathematics and will guide the learning so these may be mastered and will not become psychological blocks to the students. The wise teacher will constantly evaluate not only the progress of students but also their modes of thinking, study, and achievement, with the hope that these may be improved. Frequently the modes of work of one student will give a clue for helping those of another. Evaluation of the thinking and procedures employed by students usually is better done by careful observation and interview than by objective testing.

For effective evaluation of modes of learning, mathematics teachers must be concerned with new developments in the psychology of learning. The results of experiments must be appraised and considered for their potential use in the learning of mathematics. For example, a carefully programmed sequence presented by a mechanical device may lead a student to think and to discover; this may suggest to the teacher a new procedure for his own presentations. Or he may wish to adopt the device for certain parts of the mathematics program. The teacher who considers his present methods the best or only methods has ceased to grow and may be withholding a better method of learning from his students.

Evaluating the Mathematics of a School

Schools differ in a variety of aspects. In one school only a small part of the student body studies mathematics beyond the ninth grade, and very few obtain college scholarships and continue into the advanced study of mathematics. In another school, where the ability level of the students is not significantly better, more study mathematics and other difficult subjects, a large number continue into college, and several become distinguished scholars. Many factors account for this discrepancy, and a casual visitor can often note a difference in the tone or atmosphere of the schools. The first may have a lethargy about mathematics and about scholastic achievement in general, while the other has an atmosphere of pride in accomplishment. The differences can be identified and evaluated. Sometimes within one school the work in mathematics is distinguished, while work in other areas is mediocre. Usually the school personnel—officials and teachers—create the mathematical and scholastic climate of a school. Hence the mathematics teachers must appraise local conditions and try to establish favorable circumstances for learning. The mathematics teacher should be a prime factor in the discovery of future mathematicians and scientists. While this might well begin in elementary school, the nurture of gifted students is a continuing challenge and obligation.

Many parts of a school mathematics program such as curriculum, student achievement, teacher training, teaching procedures, and student advisement and counseling may be evaluated at least in part by objective instruments. However, certain other factors that characterize a school program must be appraised by an informed judgment based on adequate information.

Evaluation Stimulates Learning Experiences

When a student is taking a test he must think and perform operations. Usually he experiences a feeling of concern and intense concentration. His test responses are, therefore, apt to be remembered longer than a casual learning experience. When a student is quizzed informally or interviewed for purposes of evaluation, the situation can be used to foster reorganized thinking and better understanding. While students are preparing for a test, some new learning and much reinforcement of learning usually occur because it is natural to wish to establish a good record. Many teachers capitalize on these situations by reviewing and refreshing and directing work toward their goals of instruction. A good review for a test provides not only added practice but also a better understanding of the elements learned and their relation to one another. While original learning, review, and testing are taking place, the teacher should be making informal evaluations of the way students are thinking.

An additional learning experience is gained when students score their own or their colleagues' test papers. When test papers are finally returned, students should first try to discover their sources of error and then proceed to correct misunderstandings of facts, concepts, and mathematical principles, as well as errors in technical operations and computations. Whenever possible a test should be used in this way as a learning device and a means of reteaching.

Many teachers have students prepare test items. This is done for the learning experience and for the information that is revealed about the level of the student who prepared each item, rather than for the specific items obtained.

Making Use of Test Results

A teacher should use several methods of capitalizing on test results. He may select items most frequently in error for reteaching a whole unit. He may identify certain trouble spots and point out the source of difficulty. He may write corrective notes on certain papers. He may regroup the members of the class according to test results and continue accordingly. Some teachers expect their students to use the textbooks to correct certain types of errors. Other teachers give open-book tests, which check the students' ability to find and use information. This procedure reduces the necessity of memorization.

The person who prepares a test or evaluative instrument has a large responsibility. He must choose the significant concepts, principles, and operations involved in the unit being evaluated and then prepare valid test items to measure the learning. He may decide that certain types of learning are more reliably rated by his own judgment than through a test he devises. Readers of this yearbook will find many aids for the preparation and interpretation of tests in subsequent chapters.

Summary

Evaluation is considered an important part of the program in mathematics. It can serve to improve the effectiveness of a school in many different ways:

1. Evaluation can establish levels of learning and locate a student at a level suitable for his current status in mathematics.

2. Evaluation is useful in improving the mathematics program in terms of curriculum content and organization, selection of materials for learning, and modes of instruction and learning. It can furnish data which should be used in making value judgments.

3. The place of mathematics in modern society can be studied and appraised in its many ramifications, and the results of such appraisal can be used in an appreciative way and also as a factor in determining the curriculum.

4. Competent evaluation of the mathematics program of a school is useful in keeping the clientele of the school informed and in answering questions raised by critics.

5. The information and data collected in evaluation form the substance of a student's record in school. These data are useful not only for records and reports but also for research.

6. Evaluation is much concerned with helping the student learn mathematics more effectively. Hence it seeks answers to many questions dealing with the kind of mathematics, the level of learning, motivation, and aspiration.

7. Different modes of learning and their effectiveness when applied to mathematics should be evaluated. This applies to various types of materials, various levels of learning, and various types of students.

8. Finally, evaluation itself provides valuable learning experiences that a good teacher will capitalize on to enhance the work of the students.

3

Basic Principles of Evaluation

MAURICE L. HARTUNG

IN THIS CHAPTER we discuss the basic principles of evaluation. We begin by defining key terms and giving a brief description of the nature of the evaluation process. We then outline the major steps. After these introductory sections we give special emphasis to some principles useful in formulating and organizing objectives. We then direct attention to problems of securing valid records of student behavior. Assuming adequate test results or other records have been obtained, we next discuss some of the problems of interpreting these records. Finally, we present three basic criteria for evaluation programs as a whole. Of necessity, these discussions are somewhat general. The ideas are here clarified and supported by specific examples to a limited extent. Other chapters include illustrations or comments of a more detailed nature.

The Nature of the Evaluation Process

Evaluation is one of the key concepts in curriculum theory and in practical school work. Before discussing basic principles of evaluation we need some definitions. Since teachers of mathematics are well aware of the fundamental role of definitions in any theory, they should be prepared to accept a definition of *evaluation* that is based upon other key terms and upon undefined terms. Other key terms for our discussion are *experience* and *objective*. The undefined terms are *behavior* and *situation*.

We define *experience* as behavior in specified situations. Although we shall not define *behavior,* we note that it is classified into three major types: thinking, feeling, and acting in some physical way. In the technical terminology of the psychologists these types of behavior are called cognitive, affective, and motor. *Behavior* is broader than *deportment* and similar terms sometimes used to describe students' tendencies to conform or to fail to conform to school rules and regulations.

Teachers are concerned with the behavior of their students at specified times and in specified places—in school and, in some cases, out of school and in later life. The term *situation* covers the relevant facts relating to behavior. It also covers the subject matter, or content, with which the instruction is concerned. Consider the following sentence: "Johnny, who is a student at Washington School, learned yesterday how to construct a regular hexagon, and he felt satisfaction." This sentence tells us that Johnny had a bit of experience. It mentions briefly a situation (a person, a place, and a time) and some behavior that occurred in the situation. The behavior centered on mathematical content. Even in this simple example the behavior undoubtedly involved thinking, feeling (he "felt satisfaction"), and motor activity in complex interaction.

Objectives are desired experiences. This definition of the term *objective* is precise, but perhaps deceptively simple. We shall avoid other terms such as *goals, purposes, outcomes,* that are sometimes used in discussions of objectives and evaluation.

Students have many experiences their teachers do not want them to have. For example, a teacher may justifiably believe the class needs some practice or drill to acquire skill. The students may do an assignment and learn from it, but those students who most need the practice may dislike the activity. The *dislike* part of the experience is rarely desired; that is, dislike of mathematics is not an objective. Ideally, the experiences desired by teachers for students are also desired by the students themselves. We can say that both students and teachers should have the same objectives. In a discussion of curriculum and methods it would be relevant to consider ways of achieving this ideal, but such a consideration is out of place here.

Evaluation and Measurement

Evaluation may now be defined as the process of finding the extent to which the actual experiences conform to the objectives. It will be useful at this point to note a distinction between evaluation and measurement. In education the term *measurement* refers to the process of gathering certain types of data for the purpose of evaluation. It also includes part of the process of analysis and interpretation, but not all of it. The calculation of the mean score for a class that has taken a test is part of the measurement process. The interpretation of this score will usually carry one into the broader domain of evaluation. Interpretation may require value judgments that are based on the value position or educational philosophy of the teacher or school. It is this aspect of the process that led to the adoption, during the 20-year period following 1934, of the term *evaluation* for the complete process.

Another term used in connection with evaluation is *appraisal*. It refers to a comparison of the measured achievement of one group of students with the achievement of other, presumably comparable groups.

Change—the Aim of Education

More basically, however, the purpose of education is to change students from a given state of experience to a desired state by means of a variety of appropriate learning experiences, some of which may be used as a basis for evaluation of achievement. To evaluate in this way, we measure at intervals and try to determine whether any change has occurred in the students. As time goes on, do they exhibit more or less of the desired behavior? Do they have deeper understanding of mathematical concepts? Do they have some concepts in June that they did not have in September? Do they appreciate mathematics more this year than they did last year? When we evaluate, we find answers to such questions, and we make judgments as to whether the amount and direction of change is satisfactory. We also render judgment as to whether the performance is typical for a given situation and whether it is indicative of maximum performance. Evaluation is the means we use to discover where we stand on the path between present experience and the objective.

Steps in the Evaluation Process

Evaluation proceeds through a sequence of steps, and after these steps have been taken once, they are repeated in cyclical fashion. At least the first two are part of curriculum planning in general; they have to be taken even if no formal evaluation is contemplated. We shall outline and comment briefly on the steps in evaluation.

Formulating Objectives

The first step is adequate formulation of the objectives for evaluation purposes. Most lists of objectives are inadequate. Often they are not so formulated that the teacher and student both know clearly what is expected. In a later section we shall discuss some criteria for an adequate formulation. Objectives related to specific test items are given in Chapter 5.

Selecting Test Situations

The second step is the selection of sample situations in which the desired student behavior may legitimately be expected. Although we can often set up a problem or test situation easily and put the student to work at it, this is not possible for all types of objectives. For those related to interest in mathematics, for example, our behavioral descriptions may require questions such as the following: *Does the student voluntarily look for and read books, magazine articles, and newspaper stories that deal with mathematics? Does he try to work unassigned problems? Does he try to discover mathematical relationships that are new at least to him?* The situations suggested by these questions involve out-of-school as well as in-school activity. Such situations are not subject to control by the teacher and give rise to difficult problems in evaluation.

Recording Data

The third major step is obtaining a record of what happens in the sample situations. When we ask a student to take a written test, he usually makes his own record on the answer sheet. In other situations securing the record is more difficult and may require interviewing, observation of the student, or other techniques in which the record is made by someone other than the student. In all cases, however, the idea is the same—we need a permanent record of the behavior in order to proceed with subsequent steps in the process.

Analyzing and Interpreting the Record

The fourth major step is the analysis and interpretation of the record. This is very easy in some situations; in others it may require sophisticated statistical or psychological techniques, auxiliary data such as norms, and sound judgment based on considerable experience.

Determining Changes

The fifth major step, for which the others are preparation, justifies the entire process. It consists in determining desirable changes in objectives, learning activities and instructional methods, techniques of evaluation, materials and facilities, and other aspects of the curriculum.

If everything is judged to be satisfactory (a rare event), attention may be turned to new objectives. If not, the cycle is, in theory, repeated under changed conditions. In this way the process contributes to steady improvement of the curriculum and to other purposes discussed in Chapter 2.

With these steps and the general nature of the evaluation process in mind, we are now ready to look into some principles that increase the effectiveness of the evaluation.

Principles for the Formulation of Objectives

The formulation of objectives is perhaps the most important of all the tasks of the educator. Unfortunately, this task is often viewed with distaste, perhaps because relatively few teachers have formulated objectives under conditions favorable for producing a really good set and becoming aware of the profound effects it can have on teaching. In this section we discuss some of the ideas that should govern the formulation of objectives.

As a preliminary to this task the teacher must have a set of data that describes the situation in part. These data include information about the students who are to be taught and whose experience is to be evaluated. Usually the age, grade or class in school, intelligence test score, and similar facts are needed. Sometimes other types of data are also relevant. For example, data on reading achievement, dominant interests, vocational ambitions, and physical handicaps may be needed to determine the relevance of the behavior and the subject-matter content.

Content

The most familiar aspect of a set of objectives is the specification of the subject matter that is to be learned. Many lists of so-called objectives consist primarily of items of content. They include such technical terms or names of concepts as *sum, quotient, factor, exponent, theorem,* and *perpendicular;* they include facts, principles, and theorems to be remembered; formulas to be recalled; constructions to be made; and similar types of content. Specifications of this kind are necessary, but they are not sufficient.

There must also be a description of the behavior the student is expected to learn. The question is: *What kind of thinking, feeling, or action is desirable in this situation?* The behavioral description uses such terms as *recall, understand, apply, analyze, appreciate,* and *reason logically.*

Sample Objectives

As a sample of objectives recently put forth by a highly competent and authoritative group, consider the following (2:11):*

More specifically, some objectives of mathematics in general education are:

1. An understanding of, and competence in, the processes of arithmetic and the use of formulas in elementary algebra. A basic knowledge of graphical methods and simple statistics is also important.

2. An understanding of the general properties of geometrical figures and the relationships among them.

3. An understanding of the deductive method as a method of thought. This includes the ideas of axioms, rules of inference, and methods of proof.

4. An understanding of mathematics as a continuing creative endeavor with aesthetic values similar to those found in art and music. In particular, it should be made clear that mathematics is a living subject, not one that has long since been embalmed in textbooks.

Although these objectives are relatively general, they specify both behavior ("understanding") and particular types of subject matter ("the processes of arithmetic," "the general properties of geometrical figures," and so on) with which the behavior is to be associated. At the same time these statements involve certain terms ("competence," "knowledge") which need further elaboration. Without such definition every teacher will supply his own interpretation, and wide variation in what is considered satisfactory achievement may result.

From statement 1 of the objectives quoted above, one may derive others that are more specific. As a useful first step we may separate the compound statements into simpler expressions as follows:

(*a*) Understanding the processes of arithmetic
(*b*) Competence in the processes of arithmetic
(*c*) Understanding the use of formulas in elementary algebra
(*d*) Competence in the use of formulas in elementary algebra
(*e*) Basic knowledge of graphical methods
(*f*) Basic knowledge of simple statistics.

Let us now focus our attention on statements (*c*) and (*d*).

Measuring the Attainment of an Objective

One approach to specification is to list formulas that may be studied or used as examples in a test. The list might include the following:

$$F = (9/5)C + 32, \quad E = mc^2, \quad S = (1/2)gt^2 + v_0t + S_0, \quad V = (4/3)\pi r^3.$$

* The symbol (*x:y*) will be used to refer to page *y* of reference *x* in the numbered list at the end of this chapter.

Lists of this sort and, more generally, of any kind of subject matter to be covered are relatively easy to prepare and may become very extensive. Given only a list of content topics or concepts, however, the teacher and curriculum maker may be uncertain as to what behavior is to be expected. The task of selecting appropriate material and instructional methods, particularly those for the evaluation of achievement, remains difficult.

Recalling Formulas

Is the student expected to *recall* the formula ($F = (9/5)C + 32$, for example)? If so, we may tell him to memorize it, and in a test situation we might ask him to "write a formula that states a relation between temperature as measured by the Centigrade scale and temperature as measured by the Fahrenheit scale." Many modern teachers would not consider this behavior particularly desirable. To them, *understand* means something different from *remember,* and the recall of a specific scientific formula is less important than a more general concept of formulas. The behavior indicated by the sentence "The student can use formulas as guides in calculation" probably comes closer to revealing understanding. This sentence may be stated even more specifically as follows: "The student can systematically replace 'independent' variables in a mathematical sentence with names of numbers"; and "The student is able to carry through without error mathematical operations indicated by symbols in a formula." More briefly, the student must be able to substitute and compute. But does this ability really indicate understanding?

Applying Formulas

A more demanding type of behavior is applying an appropriate formula in solving a problem. This formulation covers the ability to analyze a new problem situation, to recognize that a particular formula is applicable, to recall the formula, and to use it as a guide in calculation. Since these behaviors include those mentioned earlier, which must be integrated in a problem-solving procedure, successful performance is much more likely to be based on understanding.

Deriving Formulas

Continuing, suppose we specify that the desired behavior is to be able to derive the formula. This ability may or may not reveal understanding, since in some cases it means only that the student is able to put on paper or chalkboard a derivation memorized from a textbook. If the student makes his own derivation, however, his behavior may usually be considered evidence of genuine understanding.

Understanding Formulas

If the statement of the objective is left at the level indicated by *understands the use of formulas,* interesting issues arise when particular formulas from a content list are considered. For example, suppose the list includes $E = mc^2$. Some of the more specific behaviors discussed above may be called for, but do we expect students to understand this formula in terms of its physical meaning? Do we expect them to be able to derive it? These demands call for a level of mathematical and scientific maturity that would rarely be found in secondary school students. A little reflection will show that the sort of behavior expected varies from item to item of the subject matter, and the objectives are imperfectly formulated unless the relation between behavior and subject-matter elements is indicated. As a summary, then, we state that the task of formulating objectives involves not only the specification of content elements and of behavioral elements, but also the establishment of relations between the two sets of elements.

Criteria for Stating Objectives

The above discussion leads to a first criterion for the statement of an objective:

1. EACH STATEMENT OF AN OBJECTIVE SHOULD INDICATE BOTH THE DESIRED BEHAVIOR AND THE TYPE OF SITUATION IN WHICH IT IS TO OCCUR.

A second criterion for the statement of objectives is the following:

2. OBJECTIVES SHOULD BE STATED IN TERMS OF DESIRED STUDENT BEHAVIOR RATHER THAN TEACHER BEHAVIOR.

The second criterion focuses attention upon what the student is to do—how he is to think, to feel, to act. The task of the teacher is to try to arrange the learning situation so that students have an opportunity to behave in the ways specified by the objectives. Desirable student behavior is the goal, and teacher behavior is only a means to achieving the goal. Attention to this criterion tends to modify and enrich the nature of the learning activities selected by the teacher. Moreover, it is primarily student behavior that is to be evaluated, and attention to this criterion facilitates the evaluation process. Evaluation based on what the student does is virtually a prerequisite to evaluation of the competence of the teacher.

When this criterion is systematically applied, expressions such as *to teach the meaning of* . . . are revised to read *to learn the meaning of* . . ., or better, *the student remembers the meaning of* . . ., or *understands the meaning of.* . . . Many similar revisions will produce statements more precisely formulated and more useful to teachers than those tolerated when the criterion is not applied.

In this connection it may be noted that expressions such as *to gain an understanding of* . . ., and others that indicate change in behavior, need not be used in formulating objectives. If education is defined as change in behavior, the expectation of gain or change is always in view.

A diagram may help clarify this comment. Let an objective be represented by a point G. Experience is a function of time. Suppose the experience of an individual or group is determined at time t_1. Represent this

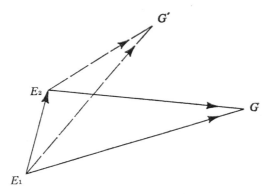

experience by the point E_1. If the actual experience is that described by the statement of the objective, the point E_1 would be the same as the point G, and no instruction may be needed. Often the actual experience is not that called for by the objective. It may be represented by a point E_1 which is not G. The amount and direction of the desired change may be considered analogous to the vector from E_1 to G. After some instruction the experience may again be determined by measurement at time t_2. Let this experience be represented by the point E_2. The vector from E_1 to E_2 may be regarded as representing the amount and direction of the actual change that occurred. The vector from E_2 to G may be interpreted as showing the amount and direction of the change still to be achieved.

It should now be observed that the objective G has not changed, and it is confusing to define the objective as a gain or change. Change (gain or loss) is what we try to measure, but is not the objective itself. To include in the statement of the objective expressions explicitly suggesting change tends to muddle the teacher's thinking about the nature of objectives and their role in measurement.

It is, of course, possible and frequently desirable to change the objective. In the diagram a different objective is indicated by the point G'. It is possible either to reduce or to increase the amount of change in experience still to be achieved merely by changing the objective without actually modifying the experience of the students in any way. It is thus desirable to distinguish between objectives (for example, the ability to make logical proofs) and changes in experience (gain in the ability to make logical proofs) that may occur.

A third criterion for the formulation of objectives is designed to control the level of specificity so that the statements are genuinely helpful in teaching. There are only a few types of general objectives, but literally hundreds of specific objectives are subsumed for even one reasonably substantial course such as algebra or geometry. The criterion seeks to mediate between the general and the specific in terms of the use to be made of objectives. It may be stated as follows:

3. OBJECTIVES SHOULD BE FORMULATED TO A LEVEL OF SPECIFICITY SUCH THAT IT IS POSSIBLE READILY TO INFER SOME LEARNING ACTIVITIES APPROPRIATE FOR HELPING STUDENTS ACHIEVE EACH OBJECTIVE AND ALSO TO DEVISE MEANS OF EVALUATING THE ACHIEVEMENT, BUT NOT TO A GREATER LEVEL OF SPECIFICITY THAN IS NEEDED FOR THESE PURPOSES.

The criterion assumes that the teacher, or whoever is formulating the objective, understands the subject matter and the nature of appropriate behavior. The criterion asserts that under these conditions the teacher should be able to plan actual lessons or, more generally, learning activities for the students. Judged by this criterion, the statement ". . . understanding of the deductive method as a method of thought" is too general to be helpful to most teachers. A more specific objective might be "understand that a deductive system must involve a set of assumptions or postulates." From this the adequately trained teacher should be able to proceed immediately to the task of lesson planning or evaluation. He might take steps to see if the students understand what is meant by the term *postulate*. He might, for example, have them look for some of the postulates stated in a mathematics textbook. He might have them study expository materials which have been written with this objective clearly in mind.

On the other hand, consider a formulation of objectives that is so specific as to list each postulate a student is expected to be able to remember and to state. Although such a formulation clearly suggests learning activities ("memorize the statements") and a way of testing achievement ("write the statements from memory"), many teachers would justifiably consider this sort of formulation to be overly prescriptive for their students. They might, for example, prefer to put the emphasis on understanding and application rather than on formal recall of this particular subject matter.

Teachers have frequently expressed dissatisfaction with published statements of objectives. Much of the dissatisfaction comes from failure of the statements to meet the criterion for optimum specificity. Perhaps another example will present more cogently the case for attention to this criterion. Objectives calling for "appreciation of mathematics" are frequently listed. Sometimes the formulation is more explicit. It may, for example, specify "appreciation of the power of mathematical methods." As a rule, however, objectives of this sort fail to satisfy the criterion for level of specificity.

When the behavior associated with "appreciation" is analyzed, it is found that more specific behaviors such as the following are involved: *wants more of; wants to know more about; speaks favorably to others about; attempts to imitate or to create more examples of.* These expressions may be completed by annexing specific items of mathematical content. Thus the original formulation of the objective might be "appreciation of the Hindu-Arabic system of numeration." The objective is clarified if the teacher interprets this to mean that the student should want more experience with the Hindu-Arabic system of numeration and should want to know more about the Hindu-Arabic system of numeration. Then the teacher may decide to use an instructional unit on numeration with bases other than ten. Moreover, the teacher may see that evaluation now is more feasible, since a variety of learning activities and many different bases for the numeration are readily available. The hypothesis is that appreciation of the Hindu-Arabic system of numeration will be enhanced if the student sees how the same principles are used when the base is not the familiar ten.

Objectives that are stated at a level of generality comparable to "appreciation of mathematics" rarely get adequate attention in the classroom. Only when the objectives are more specifically formulated can the teacher decide how to teach for them and evaluate achievement of them.

Organizing Objectives by Classification

The large number of objectives of most programs makes a cumbersome list. It is customary, therefore, to classify the statements. One such classification is in terms of types of behavior. Thus objectives involving knowledge (recall, understand) are grouped together, along with objectives involving various intellectual abilities (comprehend and interpret, apply in new situations, analyze, synthesize and generalize, evaluate) (1:204-207). Objectives involving affective behavior (interests and appreciations, attitudes and values) form a second group. Motor (or psychomotor) behaviors form a third group. Objectives of the third type are rare in mathematics education, and are confined largely to the development of skill in using instruments such as compasses and in sketching geometric figures. Some teachers would include in this category certain objectives relating to the effective oral and written presentation of proofs.

In mathematics education the familiar subject-matter classifications are much more commonly used than the behavioral types. Thus one finds lists of objectives classified as arithmetic, algebra, geometry, trigonometry, or general mathematics. Somewhat less common are sub-classifications in terms of year or grade in school; it may be noted that this scheme was adopted by the Commission on Mathematics of the College Entrance Examination Board for classifying the set of subject-matter elements suggested in their report (2:36-47).

In this connection three points need comment. First, the descriptive headings of the classification scheme are not to be confused with the objectives themselves. Second, the adoption of one scheme (for example, the use of behavior types) or another tends to put the emphasis on the associated feature of the objectives, and to neglect the other aspects. Thus in classification by behavior the subject matter may be suggested only for purposes of illustration, and the coverage may be far from complete. On the other hand, in classification by type of subject matter, the associated behavior is commonly ignored or is introduced incidentally or for illustrative purposes only. It seems clear that the organization chosen for the objectives may have definite effects upon the emphasis and organization of the program and is not to be treated lightly. Finally, since the objectives themselves (rather than the classification scheme) are central to curriculum making and evaluation, any scheme adopted for expositional reasons should provide a system of cross-coding so that both the subject matter and the behavioral components may be readily brought together.

At this point we assume that a set of objectives satisfying criteria such as those outlined earlier has been selected, and that the statements have been conveniently organized. The next step in the evaluation process is to secure a valid record of student behavior.

Securing a Record of Student Behavior

By far the most common form of educational measurement involves the use of tests. Fundamentally, a test puts a student in a certain situation and elicits certain behavior. In mathematics classes the situations are primarily mathematical, and the student makes his own record in writing. Other chapters of this yearbook discuss principles for selecting tests, preparing test items, and many other specific aspects of measurement. Here we restrict the discussion to a few general principles.

First, we call attention to the fact that progress in the field of measurement has made available a wide variety of techniques. In listing these we may begin by mentioning observation of the student in various situations. The record may consist of a simple memorandum that describes the situation and the behavior. This is commonly called an anecdotal record. When the use is warranted, however, modern investigators may employ tape recorders or photographic equipment.

Conferences or interviews with students are by no means a new technique, but in recent times this technique has been greatly improved by careful pre-planning and structuring, and by the use of check lists, scales, and similar devices for recording responses. Instruments of this type are also widely used in gathering data from large groups. The ubiquitous questionnaire needs no further mention. Check lists and scales are especially useful in evaluating such projects and products as mathematical models made by students.

The technique of examining has been greatly improved during the last 25 years. A wide variety of item types and response techniques is now available. This is important, since it makes possible the measurement of complex and subtle behavior which is commonly left unmeasured through ignorance of effective methods (1:79 ff.).

The principle associated with these comments may be stated as follows: From the wide variety available, select a measurement technique that is optimally effective for the situation in which it is to be used.

Validity

The meaning of "optimally effective" may be made more explicit by using certain technical concepts from the field of measurement. Among these are *validity, relevance, reliability,* and *objectivity*. Thus we can say, briefly, *the measurement should be as valid as possible*. The term *validity* may be discussed under two other technical terms. One of these is *relevance*. This usually refers to the extent to which the behaviors elicited from the student, and the situations (including the subject matter) in which they occur, are those specified in the statements of objectives. The question is: Are we collecting the right kind of data?

Relevance

The relevance of data collected by means of a measuring device may be judged by a careful analysis of the ways the student must behave to respond successfully. If, for example, the measuring device is a test, it should be possible to decide whether the items require recall of information, understanding of concepts, the ability to apply principles in new problem situations, or other kinds of behavior. If the measuring device is a questionnaire that seeks data about attitudes or interests, one must try to decide whether the items will elicit statements revealing attitudes or interests.

It is important to compare the content with which the student has to work with that outlined in the objectives. The items may also be checked with the course of study (if there is one), the textbook, and similar materials. If discrepancies occur, however, the validity of the materials in relation to the objectives is often as much in question as the items of the measuring device. The analysis serves to focus attention on discrepancies and the desirability of making adjustments to insure maximum relevance.

The relevance of certain types of measuring devices may be estimated empirically by calculating coefficients of correlation with some external criterion. For example, we can check in this way the relevance of an arithmetic test used for predicting future success in a high school mathematics course. Here the criterion would be some measure of success in the high school course, such as a test taken in high school. If the data from one situation yield accurate predictions of what will be obtained in another situation, they are empirically relevant for this purpose even if the logical relationship between the two sets of data is obscure. However, accurate predictions rarely occur in the absence of logical claims for relevance.

In almost every case measurement gathers only a sample of student experience. In judging relevance, therefore, principles of sampling theory may be applied. For example, attention should be given to the representativeness of the data collected as to both behavior and subject matter.

Reliability

The other technical concept under validity is reliability. In this case the questions are: How accurate are our measurements? How stable are they? Will we get approximately the same results if we immediately remeasure? Several statistical procedures are available for estimating reliability. These are discussed in Chapter 4. The reliability of a measuring device depends to a great extent upon the extensiveness of the sample of student experience. For example, a long test usually provides more reliable data than a short test. If individual scores are to be interpreted reliably, the reliability coefficients must be greater than those needed for the interpretation of group scores. Whenever important decisions based on measurements are to be made, sufficient testing time should be allowed to secure reliable results. It is unfortunate that even the best standardized tests are usually restricted by the demand that no more than one class period be required for their administration. Although hundreds of hours may have been spent on the learning process, often less than an hour is allocated to an important test to measure a substantial part of the experience of the student.

In careful investigations that use evaluation methods the technical aspects of validity are important. In the usual teaching situation also the validity of measurement is important, but the teacher is not in a position to check it systematically by technical methods, although he should be aware of the basic questions. When published tests or other measuring devices are used, he should examine the manuals to see what the authors claim for their instruments, and he should evaluate the evidence presented.

Objectivity

Objectivity, another important concept in measurement, refers to the extent to which different teachers or other evaluators arrive at the same conclusions from a given record. The use of a variety of objective or short-answer response techniques is now common. Many teachers seem to think these techniques are essential if objectivity is to be obtained. This is a misconception. Objectivity is possible with other kinds of response techniques, even the so-called essay test, if enough trouble is taken in scoring or evaluating responses. For certain types of records this scoring process is difficult and time consuming, but it is possible.

The evaluator's decision as to how he will spend his time and energy determines the type of response technique he will select for the students. The work required to prepare a really good short-answer test can be very great. For a single class or small group such expenditure of time may not be warranted. Instead, the time may be better spent in preparing good essay questions or gathering data in other ways, and then devoting more time to scoring and carefully analyzing the responses.

Careful scoring of the papers will yield data of adequate objectivity. Often these data are also more useful in guiding the students than the responses to hastily prepared short-answer examinations. Although the latter are easy to score and record, they are too often left unanalyzed. On the other hand, if large groups of students are to be evaluated, and if comparisons are to be made between groups widely separated in space or time, the work of preparing a good test using short-answer response techniques is necessary. In this case the time spent in the preliminary work is more than recovered by the time saved in scoring by punched stencil, machine, or other more or less mechanical techniques.

On the assumption that valid measurements have been obtained, we now turn to some comments on principles of interpretation.

Some Principles of Interpretation

The chief use of evaluation data assembled by the typical teacher is to determine a grade for the student. The score or grade is recorded in the grade book, and ultimately it is incorporated in reports to the parents and in the permanent records of the school. In theory, however, the evaluation data should be interpreted and used to guide the students as individuals and groups, and also to suggest changes in the school curriculum. When data are used in this way, grading becomes a relatively minor aspect of the evaluation process. The interpretation of the data as a whole and their use to guide decision making in curriculum problems are not only the culminating but also the most rewarding parts of the task.

Raw and Derived Scores

A single test score or other item of information about a single student is virtually useless. It takes on significance through its relations to other information. One type of interpretation involves comparing a student's experiences with respect to several different objectives. For example, we can study his achievement in relation to his interest in or appreciation of mathematics, or we can compare his recall of algebraic principles with his recall of geometric theorems. Sometimes it is possible to make interpretations by using only the raw scores of the students—for example, the number of correct responses. This may be called an absolute measure of the attainment of certain objectives. Often, however, it is desirable to replace the raw scores of each student with a derived score, which facilitates the interpretation. These derived scores may be called relative measures since the score indicates the relative position of the student with reference to a given group. Both absolute and relative scores may be used to indicate change or growth. There are several different types of derived scores. For example, raw scores on various parts of standardized achievement test batteries for elementary school subjects are commonly replaced by a grade-equivalent score. This indicates approximately the average grade level in school of a sample of pupils with a given raw score. Usually the data from different parts of a test battery reflect quite different sorts of behavior, such as skill and appreciation. The use of these grade-equivalent derived scores makes it easier for the teacher to compare the achievement of different objectives.

Another type of derived score is obtained by replacing each raw score with another score obtained by using a linear transformation. The coefficients of the formula are so chosen that the arithmetic mean of the transformed scores is some convenient number. The standard deviation of the new distribution may also be chosen arbitrarily. For example, the College Entrance Examination Board test scores are reported in terms of a distribution whose mean is 500, and whose standard deviation is 100. When so-called T-scores are used, a mean of 50 is arbitrarily chosen, and 10 is the standard deviation. A third type of derived score is obtained by replacing the raw score with its percentile rank. For example, if a student has a percentile rank of 57, his raw score exceeds 57 percent of the scores in the group.

Valid interpretations often require some knowledge of statistical concepts and methods. Unfortunately, we cannot discuss these here in any detail. The various methods of obtaining derived scores require quite simple mathematics. Teachers who are not already familiar with these methods should be able to learn them with ease, perhaps from a member of the mathematics department who might be recognized as statistical advisor for other members of the school staff.

Norms

We have been discussing interpretations involving comparisons of data on the achievement of different objectives. We can also compare one student's score with scores made by other students on the same test. Also, we can compare one class with another class, or one school with other schools. In each case we may make the comparison in terms of a single objective or a closely related group of objectives. In making comparisons of this sort, we often relate an individual's score to a norm. The norm is simply an average. The simplest norm is the median or the mean of the student's own class. Teachers and students regularly use these norms to make comparisons. If comparisons are to be made with the experience of students not in the same class, other norms are obviously needed. A standardized test is one in which a table of norms, or averages, is published by the authors for use in making comparisons. These norms are calculated by using the scores of large samples of students. They are usually based on some kind of derived scores. Thus there are grade-equivalent norms, percentile rank norms, and norms of the T-score type.

When norms are used, it is important that the person making the comparison know some fundamental facts about the samples of students whose averages, or norms, are reported. There is often an air of mystery about norms. There need not be. The intelligence of the students in the samples used, the types of schools they come from, and similar data that describe the norm population are essential to valid interpretations.

Since norms inevitably lag a number of years behind educational progress, it is especially important to know when the data on which they are based were collected. In other words, schools that are forward looking and active in improving curriculum must exercise caution in using national norms, which are usually based on composite populations from various schools with fairly standard curriculums. The relevance of the test for evaluation in a non-standard curriculum must be considered with care.

Misuse of Norms

Norms are often considered standards that all students and classes should be expected to meet. If the scores yield a normal distribution, of course half of them will be above the average. Too often this is taken as evidence that achievement is satisfactory without considering the intellectual capacity of the students, their prior experience, and other data needed for a valid interpretation. Some students or classes may legitimately be expected to achieve even better scores. On the other hand, scores below the average sometimes lead to unjustified censure of students who have achieved all that can reasonably be expected in the circumstances. Manuals for published tests usually warn against these misuses of norms, but the warnings are not always observed.

Many schools are now less concerned with their standing in relation to national norms than they formerly were. Instead, they use local norms—that is, the average of the local school population. In this way they can make comparisons in similar situations, keep track of changes that occur from time to time, and see if they are making progress toward their objectives. If the objectives are sound, this procedure is more likely to lead to an improved curriculum than is the use of invalid comparisons with national norms.

Standard Error

When the score of one student is compared with that of another, how much should the difference be before we can say with some assurance that one is definitely better than the other? Similarly, if the mean of one class is compared with that of another, how large must the difference be before we can be reasonably sure the achievement of the two groups is not the same? Many errors in interpretation are made by unsophisticated people because they cannot answer these questions. In both cases the statistical concept of standard error is involved, but the corresponding number is calculated differently. Manuals for published tests often give the standard error of measurement, which helps in answering the first question. To answer the second question we need an estimate of the standard error of the difference of the two means. This depends upon several factors, but in particular upon the number of students in each group. The error may be calculated in various ways. When differences are small, judgment of the existence of different achievement in two students or in two groups should be withheld at least until the statistical estimates have been made. Much injustice has resulted from failure to observe this principle.

The importance of comparing the achievement of different types of objectives is at present not sufficiently recognized. Efforts to improve achievement with respect to one objective affect other objectives—favorably or adversely. An increase in interest and appreciation tends to accompany an increase in understanding. Unreasonable emphasis upon formal drill may improve skill at the expense of creating a dislike for mathematics in some students—including many with high intelligence who are bored by excessive drill.

Cooperative Efforts

Much of the interpretation of evaluation data, as well as the related decision-making on curriculum problems, should be a cooperative activity carried out in a school by all the staff members who have responsibility for mathematics education. If this cooperative effort is to be successful, the focus must be on a type of analysis and discussion that is forward looking and critical without being threatening to the status of any teacher.

Examples of the use of evaluation data are included in other sections of this book.

Marks of a Good Evaluation Program

The term *evaluation program* refers to all the activity of the school staff in collecting and interpreting data for evaluation purposes. For maximum effectiveness, the program should satisfy certain criteria, some of which will now be discussed.

Comprehensiveness

First, the program should try to evaluate with respect to all the important objectives that are identified by the teachers. The term *comprehensive* is used to describe such a program. In practice, while achievement of certain objectives is formally evaluated, achievement of others is virtually ignored. Frequently only knowledge and skill are tested. Interest and appreciation, ability to apply knowledge in new situations, and similar objectives are neglected.

Balance

Second, the program should be balanced. It is possible for a program to be comprehensive but unbalanced. This occurs when achievement of all the important objectives is formally evaluated, but the emphasis on some is out of proportion to that on others.

System

Third, the program should call for systematic evaluation. This means that evaluation should take place at regular intervals so that growth may be measured. Evaluation with respect to some objectives may occur at any time of the year. For example, assume that a school plans to use a measuring instrument to gather data about interest in mathematics. This instrument may be given at any time of the year and repeated annually, or every second year, at the same time. Changes in the range and intensity of interest both of individuals and of groups may then be studied.

The traditional practice of testing just before grades must be reported has some justification when knowledge and skill are to be measured. In the case of other types of behavior, such as interests and attitudes, the changes that occur in a few days of instruction are usually very small. These experiences may be measured at any convenient time, but the program ought to insure that the measurement be systematic.

Changes Effected by Evaluation

When the implications of our criteria (comprehensiveness, balance, and system) are fully explored, their effects on the mathematics curriculum as a whole become apparent. There is, for example, the central idea of evaluating growth or change over time. Change may be defined as the difference between the experiences measured at two different times. The time span may be short, or it may be long. Attention to the complete evaluation program, as distinct from the regular quizzes and tests given by individual teachers, tends to produce more concern about change over longer time spans. The question of how students change through the entire high school course may be raised. Their retention of knowledge may be studied, and curriculum changes designed to increase retention may be introduced.

Consideration of the program as a whole also tends to bring about changes in emphasis on various types of objectives. Teachers often decide to put relatively more emphasis on understanding of concepts and relatively less emphasis on mere recall of facts and relations. They make plans for introducing instructional materials and methods designed to increase interest and appreciation of mathematics. They look for situations in which students can apply their knowledge of mathematics. They try to find ways in which the students can be stimulated to more creative kinds of learning experience.

All these ideas, if put into action, are designed to improve the mathematics curriculum as a whole, not just a particular unit or course. Do the desired changes in students really occur? Is the total experience better than it was before the change? Evaluation is the process by which we find answers to these and similar questions, and it is one of the most important of the tasks the teacher performs.

Summary

This chapter on general principles was designed to provide a foundation for the more specific and detailed discussions of various aspects of evaluation in the following chapters. The term *evaluation* is defined, the nature of the process is sketched, and the major steps are outlined. The discussion then turns to some principles governing the important task of formulating objectives to guide evaluation. We next discuss the organization of a set of objectives. Then the problem of securing a record of student behavior is taken up, and in this connection important technical concepts such as validity, relevance, and reliability are introduced. Finally, we comment on principles useful in interpreting the record and drawing conclusions about the desirability of changes in the curriculum. General principles of the sort we discuss above are of little value if they do not grow out of past experience and become guides to more effective action in the future.

References

1. Bloom, Benjamin S., editor. *Taxonomy of Educational Objectives. Hand-Book I: Cognitive Domain.* New York: Longmans, Green and Co., 1956. 207 p.

2. College Entrance Examination Board, Commission on Mathematics. *Program for College Preparatory Mathematics.* New York: the Board, 1959.

4

Constructing Achievement Tests and Interpreting Scores

JACK C. MERWIN

THE PREVIOUS CHAPTERS have emphasized the theory that evaluation can make a positive contribution to the learning of mathematics only if it is an integral part of the total learning experience, and they have pointed out the importance in evaluation of the objectives of a mathematics course. In this chapter we shall consider some evaluation techniques based on the same assumptions.

An effective evaluation procedure for a mathematics course starts prior to instruction, when the objectives of the course are stated in terms of student behavior. The teacher is then in a position to provide learning experiences designed to bring about the desired behaviors. From time to time he can assess what has been achieved by determining the extent to which his students can exhibit these behaviors. This step is clearly dependent on the objectives set forth prior to instruction. Evaluation instruments and techniques used to obtain information on achievement must be based on this interrelationship to be effective. The suggestions made in this chapter for collecting, judging, and interpreting achievement information are consistent with this role of evaluation in the mathematics education of students.

The criteria of reliability, relevance, and objectivity were presented and discussed in Chapter 3. We shall here discuss techniques of test development and test score interpretation that may be used to obtain reliable, relevant, objective information about the mathematics achievement of students.

Test Construction and Use

The construction and use of an achievement test may be viewed in terms of three steps:

1. Planning the test; making decisions about the course objectives to be covered, the type of items to be constructed, and the number of items to be used for sampling each of the objectives.
2. Preparing the situations to be presented to the students, or item writing.
3. Organizing, administering and scoring the test.

These three steps should be designed to yield reliable, relevant and objective information about the achievement of students. We shall, therefore, consider procedures that may be used in each of these steps to help obtain such information.

Planning the Test

In the development of an achievement test the course objectives to be covered by the test must first be established. The mathematics department and the individual teacher should be concerned with gathering information on *all* the course objectives, but this cannot usually be done with a single test. Information on achievement of some objectives, such as appreciations, will best be obtained through a non-testing approach; information about other objectives may be obtained through a variety of tests given at different times. Once the objectives to be covered by the test are set forth, a decision must be made as to the number of items and the types of items to be used to sample the behavior described in each objective.

To help insure that the completed test will give each objective the desired coverage, the number of items to be used for each objective should be set forth in an overall plan before actual test construction begins. This may be done easily and effectively by preparation of a table of specifications. In such a table the behavior parts of the objectives are column heads and the content parts are row heads (or vice versa). The specifications represent the number of items to be used for each objective. The completed table then serves as a guide for item construction. An example of a table of specifications is given in Table 1. Here the teacher has decided that he wants four items to sample the objective that the students be able to multiply fractions, nine items to sample the objective that they be able to change fractions to decimals, and so on.

There are no simple rules for determining the "right" number of items to use for each objective to be sampled. In making such decisions the evaluator must consider how much of the test should be devoted to each objective, and he must decide whether the interpretation of results will be in terms of each separate objective or the test as a whole. The proportion of the test to be used for each objective depends on its relative importance and on the amount of additional information on achievement of the objective that is, or will be, available. If interpretation of the

TABLE 1

A TABLE OF SPECIFICATIONS

Behavior / Content	Multiply	Divide	Reduce	Change	Find
Fractions........	4	6	4		
Fractions to percent..........				6	
Fractions to decimals.........				9	
Decimals........	8	6			
Decimals to percent..........				5	
A percent of a number.......					6
Percent one number is of another........					6

results is to be in terms of the total test score, the total number of items should be large enough to obtain reliable total scores. If the interpretation is to be a diagnosis based on individual objectives, the number of items on each objective should be large enough to give reliable information. The number of items needed depends upon the particular objective, but in general the larger the sampling of an objective, the more reliable the results. It must be recognized that a student's performance on one or two items sampling a given objective does not necessarily indicate reliably what his performance might have been on other items sampling the same objective.

The amount of time given to the administration of the test is, of course, a factor in determining the number of items. If the time is limited, the number of objectives to be covered may also have to be limited. There is nothing wrong with using a test that reliably samples only one or two important objectives.

The type of response technique, or item, should be determined pri-

marily by the behavior set forth in the objectives. From a testing standpoint this is the major reason for having objectives stated in terms of
student behavior. Essay items are used when we are concerned with
communication skills, that is, the ability to state ideas concisely and
completely within a logical organization. Problem-solving items are used
when we want to check the student's analysis, method, and solution.
Objective items such as true-false, multiple choice, and matching may be
used to test recognition of facts or relationships. Completion items are
convenient for testing recall of concepts or computational skill.

The more specific the behavior set forth in the objective, the more
likely it is that the students will be taught and tested on the same behavior; this insures the relevance of items. The objective that students
be able to demonstrate an understanding of fractions could be tested by
items calling for different types of behavior. If it is deemed important to
teach for and to test for the student's ability to exhibit specific behaviors
to demonstrate such an understanding, then the objective should be
delineated in terms of these specific behaviors. This would yield more
specific objectives, such as *add fractions, recognize proper fractions,
change mixed numbers to improper fractions,* and so on. Instruction may
then be specifically planned to develop the desired behaviors. For an
objective that can be sampled by more than one type of item, the decision
should be made on the basis of the characteristics of the various item
types. Let us look at the more important characteristics of some of the
item types that might be used in a mathematics achievement test.

Essay items require that the student produce answers. He must select
and organize the ideas he wishes to include in an answer and express these
ideas in writing. Thus, "Prove that $\sqrt{2}$ is an irrational number" is an
item that tests communication skill as well as an understanding of a
deductive proof. Essay items offer relatively few opportunities for guessing, but they provide more opportunity for bluffing than other item types.
Answers vary in degree of completeness and accuracy, and are difficult
to score objectively.

Like the essay item, the completion item requires that the student
produce an answer. Unlike the essay item, the completion item requires
that the student provide only a single word, number, or phrase. It can
generally be scored with a good deal of objectivity. Computational problems such as "Find the square root of 786," where only the answer is of
concern, may be classified as completion items.

Problem-solving items given to assess the student's procedure in reach-
ing an answer, as well as the answer itself, also require that the student
produce something. Like the essay items, they offer relatively few oppor-

tunities for guessing. The degree of objectivity with which they are scored can vary widely depending on the scoring procedure used. However, problem solving can also be measured with objective items; such items are illustrated in Chapter 5.

True-false items require that the student select rather than produce an answer. They usually take little time to answer and therefore can cover a relatively large amount of subject matter in a given length of testing time. They should be based on statements that are unequivocally and unambiguously true or false, such as "A terminating decimal is a rational number." True-false items provide many opportunities for the student to get the right answer by guessing. These items can be scored quickly and objectively.

Multiple-choice items, like true-false items, require that the student select an answer. A relatively large number of multiple-choice items can be answered in a given length of testing time. They may be used for a wide variety of objectives. The difficulty level of a multiple-choice item is related to the stem as well as to the choice of distractors presented with the right, or best, answer. Compared with essay items, multiple-choice items provide more opportunity for guessing and less opportunity for bluffing. Like the true-false items, they can be scored quickly with a high degree of objectivity.

Matching items require that the student select rather than supply an answer. To be effective the responses must be sufficiently homogeneous so that the correct response for one premise constitutes a plausible distractor for another premise. Matching items can be quickly and objectively scored.

Item Writing

After decisions have been made regarding the objectives to be covered and the type and number of items for each objective, the next step is item writing—the preparation of situations to be presented to the student to elicit his behavior. There are certain basic considerations in item writing for achievement tests. We must remember that any test will provide only a sampling of behaviors set forth in the course objectives. The job of any single item is to separate those students who have in large degree attained the objective sampled (the "Cans") from those students who have not, to any extent, reached it (the "Cannots"). Each item marked right or wrong divides students into a dichotomy. Anything about the structure and presentation of the item that leads the Cans to get it wrong or the Cannots to get it right will lead to false information. Let us consider this from the standpoint of the student.

On each item the student is expected to use all the knowledge, skill, imagination and intuition he can muster to find the answer that will identify him as a Can. Any consistent strategy, conscious or otherwise, used in item construction can be used by students in answering the items. Some students feel, in preparing for tests, that it is just as important to learn the teacher as it is to learn mathematics. For example, suppose the student knows, even though the teacher may not, that on true-false tests the teacher generally has more true than false items. When a Cannot doesn't know the answer to an item and marks it *true* on this basis, he will very likely be identified as a Can if the teacher is following his usual pattern. If the student knows that the teacher very often uses items with answers that are whole numbers, though he may be a Cannot in terms of the objective, he may get the item correct through locating the "right" process to use on the item—the one that gives a whole number. The student may know that if he gives a long enough answer to an essay item he will be given some, if not full, credit whether or not it is the answer the teacher is after. All such tools of the "test-taker's trade" are strictly legal. Therefore the teacher must constantly be aware of irrelevant clues he builds into items.

As an aid to minimizing the number of irrelevant clues built into test items a teacher may use established rules for item writing. A number of these rules are specific to particular item types while others are applicable in the writing of various item types. Since rules for item writing are presented with discussion and examples in a number of sources (2, 5, 7, 8), we shall consider here only a few basic rules that are generally applicable.

1. MAKE EVERY EFFORT TO AVOID AMBIGUITIES. If you state an item so that more than one interpretation is possible, a student who has reached the objective may select the wrong interpretation and give an incorrect answer. State the item in precise mathematical language appropriate to the students involved. In every case, use proper grammatical construction. Every item should be carefully scrutinized for any reasonable interpretation other than the one intended. For example:

The area of a circle is equal to pi times one-fourth of the diameter squared.

A true-false item stated in this way leaves even the student who knows the relationship in an ambiguous position. If he interprets the item as saying that one-fourth of the diameter is squared, he will mark the item false. If he interprets it as saying that only the diameter is squared, he will mark it true. A little rewording avoids this difficulty:

The area of a circle is equal to pi times one-fourth of the square of the diameter.

2. AVOID THE USE OF EXCESSIVE WINDOW DRESSING. Do not put any more in an item than is necessary for the purposes of that item. At times you may be interested in testing the student's ability to select relevant information, and in this case the inclusion of irrelevant information is in line with the purpose of the item. In general, however, avoid the inclusion of irrelevant information unless ability to recognize it as such is being tested. For example:

Since the circumference of a circle is equal to pi times the diameter, and the area of a circle is equal to pi times the square of the radius, what is the value of pi?

This item does not specifically call for a numerical answer, though that may be what is desired. The superfluous information might cause the good student to wonder whether the desired answer is in terms of the circumference and area $(C^2/4A)$, in terms of the circumference and the diameter (C/D), in terms of the area and radius (A/R^2), or any one of a number of possible numerical approximations. If the desired answer is a numerical approximation, an improved statement would be simply:

To the nearest hundredth what is the value of pi?

3. AVOID THE USE OF LONG AND INVOLVED STATEMENTS. Such statements will present some of your students with a time-consuming problem of digging out the elements that are important in answering the item. They should be simplified or broken into a few simple statements. For example:

Since vectors expressed in polar form must be added by graphical methods, while vectors expressed in terms of their rectangular components can be added algebraically, express the vectors $(8, \frac{\pi}{2})$ $(14, 0)$ in their rectangular components and find their sum algebraically.

This item would be improved if simply stated:

Change the vectors $(8, \frac{\pi}{2})$ $(14, 0)$ to their rectangular components and find their sum algebraically.

4. SPECIFY THE DEGREE OF ACCURACY REQUIRED FOR FULL CREDIT WHERE APPROXIMATE ANSWERS ARE DESIRED. You can specify the degree of accuracy either in the item or in the directions for a series of similar items. Consider the following:

If a parking lot that can hold 300 cars now has 35 cars in it, what part of the lot is vacant?

Here some students may give the exact answer, 265/300, and others may give decimal answers to various degrees of accuracy. If the teacher wants this item answered to the nearest hundredth, it may be written:

A parking lot that can hold 300 cars now has 35 cars in it. To the nearest hundredth, what part of the lot is vacant?

5. AVOID EXTRANEOUS CLUES. Check carefully for information a student can use to get an item right even though he does not have the abilities the item is sampling. Often such clues are given in the way an item is worded. For example:

In the expression, 3^x, the "x" would be called an
1. root
2. base
3. radical
4. exponent

Here the right answer is the only alternative that correctly follows the article *an*. Even if this were a completion item the first three alternatives could be eliminated as possibilities by many students. An improvement would be:

In the expression 3^x, the "x" would be called
1. a root
2. a base
3. a radical
4. an exponent

6. AVOID GIVING CLUES TO ONE ITEM IN THE STATEMENT OF ANOTHER. When you attempt to get at an objective from many different angles, this needs particular attention. Consider the following two items which might appear on the same test, though not necessarily following one another:

Which of the following is a special type of quadrilateral?
1. rhombus
2. pentagon
3. regular hexagon
4. triangle

Which of the following quadrilaterals is by definition equiangular?
1. trapezoid
2. rhombus
3. square
4. parallelogram

Most students would expect that all the alternatives given for the second item are quadrilaterals. Rhombus would appear to be a reasonable selection for the first item based on its appearance in the second. This difficulty could be avoided by deleting or replacing rhombus as an alternative in the second item.

7. AVOID THE USE OF NEGATIVE STATEMENTS WHENEVER POSSIBLE, AND NEVER USE DOUBLE NEGATIVES. Negations in the statement of items are easily missed by students, particularly when speed is a factor. When a student who has reached the objective misses a negation, he will get the

item wrong. You can reword most negative statements as positive statements. For example, consider the following true-false item:

The number 99, base ten, cannot be expressed using two digits with an integer base less than ten or greater than ninety-nine.

The negation can be removed without changing the answer by rewording:

The number 99, base ten, can be expressed using two digits only with an integer base that is greater than nine and less than one hundred.

When negative statements cannot be avoided, call the negation to the attention of the students by capitalization, underlining or both (NOT).

Carefully check all your items for incorrect mathematics, incorrect grammar, or trick questions that have a twist relatively unimportant to the objective.

Organizing, Administering and Scoring the Test

After items are prepared, the next step is organizing them into a test. There are two major considerations in setting up the test: (*a*) the ease with which the student can understand what he is to do, and where and how he is to record his answers, and (*b*) the ease with which the teacher will be able to locate and score the answers. The following general rules have been found helpful:

Grouping Items. Put all items of the same type together (that is, all multiple-choice items together, all computational items together, all true-false items together, and so on). Number all items consecutively from the first item on the test to the last.

Arrange each subdivision of the test so that the easier items come before the more difficult ones.

Avoid putting part of an item on the bottom of a page and the remainder on the top of the next page. Be sure that each item is legible.

Directions. Precede each group of items with a simple and clear statement telling how and where the student is to indicate his answers. For computational items the directions might be, "For each problem below write your answer to the nearest hundredth on the line in front of the problem number."

Directions for computational items requiring answers in denominate numbers should state that the denomination is required for full credit.

Directions for multiple-choice items should tell the student whether he is to seek the *right* answer or the *best* answer.

Directions for true-false or multiple-choice items should inform the student if any correction for guessing will be used in scoring.

If the method of arriving at the answer will be used in evaluating performance, include a statement indicating that work should be shown and will be considered in the scoring.

Recording of Answers. It is generally desirable to provide answer spaces that correspond with the placement of the items on the page. When separate answer sheets are used, the answer spaces may be put in columns, one column for each page of items. The student may then place the answer sheet under the test booklet and line the answer spaces up with the items on each page. The use of separate answer sheets reduces the labor of scoring, particularly when the test covers three or more pages.

If students answer the problems on the test booklet, place answer spaces down the side of the page (see Fig. 1). This will reduce the labor of scoring.

If computational work leading to answers is to be used in scoring, leave space for computation near the answer space for each item.

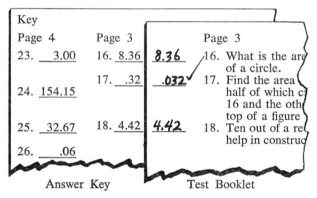

Figure 1. Example of the use of a scoring key when answers are marked on the test booklet.

Administration. Have each student work from a separate copy of the test, rather than from a test written on the blackboard. Have all necessary materials on hand such as scratch paper, erasers, and pencils. Provide the best possible physical surroundings, with adequate light, ventilation and desk space.

If speed is not a factor in the objectives covered by the test, be sure that enough time is allowed so that each student has an opportunity to attempt all the items.

Scoring the Test. Prepare a key containing all the answers that are to be given credit. If the items are carefully prepared, there may be only one acceptable answer for each item. If the ambiguity of a statement makes two or more answers acceptable, they should be included on the key.

Prepare a list of acceptable answers in such a way that it can be placed beside the answer spaces used by the students (see Fig. 1).

In scoring essay tests, objectivity is generally increased if (a) a model answer for each item is prepared ahead of time and used in the same way in scoring each paper, (b) the identity of the student who wrote each answer is not known at the time of scoring, and (c) each item is scored for all papers before going on to the next item.

It is often impossible to make fine discriminations among answers to essay items. In scoring each such item, merely sorting the papers into 4 or 5 piles and giving the same item score to all papers in a pile may be adequate.

Analysis of Test Scores for Interpretation

The set of scores from an achievement test can be tabulated, summarized, and analyzed to provide many different types of information. Here we shall consider three types of information we may obtain from test scores: information about the achievement of the class, information about the achievement of individual students, and information about the test.

Test scores are sometimes used as evidence of the effectiveness of methods, materials, and the curriculum. Such use can lead to erroneous conclusions unless we account for other variables affecting achievement, such as the ability of the group. Research studies that may be designed to control for the effect of such other factors are beyond the scope of the present discussion.

Information about the Achievement of the Class

Generally most useful to a teacher is information concerning the level of performance of the class, the extent to which scores differ, and the performance of individual students. The level of performance of a class may be summarized in a measure of central tendency, such as the mean. The spread of the scores is indicated by a measure of dispersion, such as the standard deviation. These measures may be used as a basis for interpreting the score of an individual student and for comparing the scores of two or more groups taking the same test.

Measures of Central Tendency. Three measures of central tendency that may be used in analyzing test scores are the arithmetic mean, the median and the mode. The arithmetic mean, usually shortened to *mean,* is commonly referred to as the average. The median is the score, or point on the score scale, that has half of the scores above it and half below it. The mode is the score that occurs most frequently.

The shape of the score distribution affects the relative size of the mean and median, as illustrated in Table 2. When to use the mean and when to use the median as the measure of central tendency may be summarized as follows: (*a*) If the distribution is symmetrical (Test B results), use either measure, since the mean and the median will be numerically equal. (*b*) If the distribution is asymmetrical or skewed (Test A or Test C results), and it is desirable to minimize the contribution of the extreme scores, use the median. (*c*) If the distribution is asymmetrical, and the contribution of each score is to be in direct relation to its size, use the mean.

TABLE 2

THREE FREQUENCY DISTRIBUTIONS WITH
EQUAL MEDIANS, DIFFERENT SHAPES AND DIFFERENT MEANS

Test A			Test B			Test C	
Score	Frequency		Score	Frequency		Score	Frequency
10	6		13	1		16	1
9	9		12	2		15	1
8	4		11	3		14	1
7	3		10	4		13	2
6	2		9	5		12	1
5	1		8	5		11	2
4	2		7	4		10	3
3	1		6	3		9	4
2	1		5	2		8	9
1	1		4	1		7	6
	30			30			30

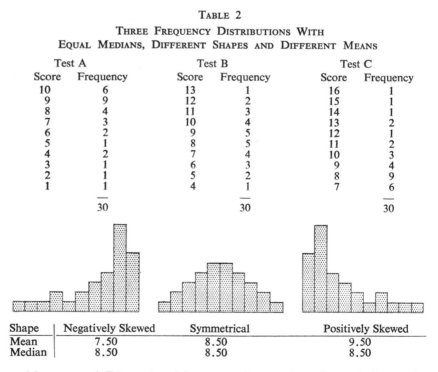

Shape	Negatively Skewed	Symmetrical	Positively Skewed
Mean	7.50	8.50	9.50
Median	8.50	8.50	8.50

Measures of Dispersion. Measures of central tendency indicate the performance of the group as a whole, but this is often a very sketchy picture of a set of scores. Some measure of dispersion is also needed to indicate the amount of spread, or scattering, of the scores. The way measures of dispersion reflect the spread of scores of different groups taking the same test is illustrated in Table 3. The mean and median are both 5.5 for each of these distributions, although the distributions are obviously quite different and much of the difference is reflected in a measure of dispersion.

The range is a simple, easily-obtained measure of dispersion. It is often defined as the difference between the highest and lowest scores. The main disadvantage of the range as a measure of dispersion is that it tells nothing about the scatter of the scores between the extremes. In this respect the standard deviation is a much better measure of dispersion.

TABLE 3

MEASURES OF DISPERSION FOR THE SCORES OF
THREE GROUPS OF STUDENTS: WITH VARYING AMOUNTS
OF SCATTER ON THE SAME TEST

Score	Group I Frequency	Group II Frequency	Group III Frequency
10	1		
9	1		
8	1	1	
7	1	1	
6	1	3	5
5	1	3	5
4	1	1	
3	1	1	
2	1		
1	1		
	10	10	10
Range	9	5	1
Standard Deviation	2.87	1.36	.50

The standard deviation takes into account the deviation of each score from the mean. In addition to its usefulness as a measure of dispersion, it may also be used, as we shall see in the next section, in describing the test performance of individuals.

The central tendency and dispersion of a set of scores are determined by many factors. The level of ability and differences in ability of the students tested, the characteristics of the test, and the conditions under which the test is administered are prime factors. The teacher will have a general idea of the ability level of the group and can usually select and structure the testing conditions. He can, therefore, select or construct a test that should, in light of other factors, yield roughly the distribution of results he is seeking.

How the test results will be used determines the kind of distribution sought. To illustrate this, consider the difference in two situations. One

teacher is giving a test to identify students needing diagnosis and remedial work. A relatively easy test that spreads the low ability students
and bunches the rest at perfect or near perfect scores will serve his
purpose. A second teacher wants a test that will measure the achievement of all of his students. This teacher will want a distribution with
enough spread to show differences among all students and with a central tendency such that the best student and the poorest student will
both be adequately measured.

Information About the Achievement of Individuals

No test score has meaning in itself. It is little help to know, for example, that an elementary pupil received 64 points on an arithmetic
test. It adds little to know there were 150 possible points. We must
know how other students achieved on the test. The achievement of a
group of students adds meaning to the individual score, for it provides
a basis for comparison. These *other* students are called norm groups.
If, in the illustration given above, we know that the average score in
a specified normative group is 50, we may say our particular student
is probably above the average for that norm group.

Since the term *norm* suggests a basic comparison group, it is obvious
that any normative group will not do. At the same time the importance
of specifying the normative group used is also apparent.

The following normative groups would be among those to be considered for a particular mathematics test:

1. The mathematics class of which a student is one member.
2. All the mathematics classes or students of a particular grade or
   age level in a particular school, or a representative random sample.
3. All the mathematics classes or students of a particular grade or
   age level in a particular community, or a representative random
   sample.
4. All mathematics classes or students of a particular grade or age
   level in a broad geographic area—a state, or a combination of
   states or countries—or a representative random sample.

It is usually wise to develop local norms (class, school, or community)
for basic achievement or aptitude tests. Local norms take into account
such unique community situations as variation in socio-economic level
and in curriculum pattern. On some tests of quantitative achievement,
entire classes may rank in the upper 10 percent on national norms.
If in a particular school only the brightest students take geometry,
we expect these students to rank high when compared with a less selected

national group. If an arithmetic test is administered to a group of 9-year-olds, we do not expect them to rank high when compared with 10- and 11-year-olds.

At the same time we may, in some situations, wish to compare an individual or class with a norm group that has characteristics different from his own. For example, we might wish to compare a bright 12-year-old with a national sample of 15-year-olds to ascertain his achievement in algebra.

In order to use norms intelligently we need a clear definition and description of the norm group and a clear definition and description of the group or individual to be compared with the norm. Any conclusion must then relate to the characteristics of both groups.

A student's score on an achievement test is sometimes interpreted in terms of a comparison with the highest possible score on the test. This method usually expresses the score as a percentage. Some of the characteristics of this approach make it very unsatisfactory.

First, it is extremely difficult, if not impossible, to build into a test exactly the difficulty level desired. If a student gets 80 percent of the highest possible score on a test, it is highly improbable that he would get 80 percent of the highest possible score on a second test constructed to cover the same objectives. Second, any achievement test will cover only a sampling of the behaviors set forth in the course objectives. Most teachers, quite naturally, are not content to restrict their interpretation of the student's test score to his ability on the particular test items. They want to expand the interpretation to make an inference about what the student *can do* in terms of what he *did* on the test. Let us explore this briefly.

An inference that the student who gets 75 percent of a test right has mastered 75 percent of the material covered in the course would generally be inaccurate due to many factors. The difficulty level of the test, the adequacy with which the test samples *all* the objectives to be covered, the extent to which the results are affected by the time and conditions under which the test is administered, and the degree of subjectivity that enters into the scoring—all play a part in determining a student's score. Since we do not know the extent to which each of these factors is reflected in a score of 75 percent, such a score is not very meaningful.

To increase the amount of information obtained from a test score, we may interpret a student's performance on a test through the use of derived scores. A derived score indicates a student's performance in terms of the performance of other students. A major advantage of derived scores over raw scores is their comparability across different tests given to the same group of students. Even though two tests given in a course may have quite different levels of difficulty and numbers of items, a student's derived scores from the two tests may be considered comparable if both are based on the same group of students. When a teacher has four or five test scores for each of the students in a class, the set of raw scores for a given individual are not readily comparable; his percentage score of 95 may be an average performance on a fairly easy test, his 78 may be an outstanding performance on a difficult test, and so on. Derived scores are a means of taking into account such problems of interpretation.

A major consideration in the use of derived scores is that they are dependent upon the particular group on which they are based. A student's performance on a test could be outstanding when compared with one group and only average when compared with another group, as we pointed out in the discussion of norms. This is not a serious problem for most classroom tests, however, since the derived scores for all tests used in a course are generally based on the same group of students.

There are many different procedures that may be used to establish derived scores. Here we shall consider three types of derived scores: ranks, percentile ranks, and standard scores. Ranks are the most readily obtained of the three.

Ranks for students may be obtained by putting the papers in order according to the raw scores and numbering them from the best to the poorest. The person with the highest score has a rank of 1, next highest a rank of 2, and so forth. Where ties occur, the people tied in raw scores are given the same rank, the mean of the ranks they would have if they were not tied. For example, in the distribution in Table 4 the 15th and 16th students are tied. They both receive a rank of 15.5, the person just above having a rank of 14 and the person just below having a rank of 17. Ease of computation is the main advantage of the use of ranks as derived scores. There are several disadvantages.

One limitation of the use of ranks is that they mask the size of the differences in the raw scores. For example, the three top students in the distribution of scores in Table 4 have scores of 59, 53, and 52, their ranks being 1, 2, and 3, respectively, even though six score points separate the top two and only one point separates the second and third highest. A second limitation is that the interpretation of a rank depends on the number of students involved in the ranking. If a student has a rank of 12 in a class of 12, it is interpreted differently from the way it is if the class has 40 students. This is not a serious limitation if a teacher is concerned with the ranks of the same students from test to test.

Percentile ranks, like ranks, provide an ordering of students in a group. A student's percentile rank, however, provides this information in terms of the percent of the group having scores lower than his. Thus, if John has a raw score of 72, and 34 percent of his classmates have scores below 72, John's percentile rank is 34. If Susan's percentile rank is 85, we know that 85 percent of the class have scores lower than hers. It is important to note that Susan's percentile rank of 85 gives no information about how many items she answered correctly. She may have answered almost all of the items correctly or she may have answered only a few of the items correctly. The raw score depends on the difficulty of the test. Regardless of the difficulty of the test, the percentile rank of 85 indicates that Susan scored higher than 85 percent of her classmates.

TABLE 4

DERIVED SCORES CORRESPONDING TO A SET OF RAW SCORES

Score	Frequency	Rank	Percentile Rank	Standard Scores	
				z-score	Transformed z-score
				Mean = 0	Mean = 50
				S.D.* = 1	S.D. = 10
59	1	1	96	1.62	66
53	1	2	92	.90	59
52	1	3	88	.78	58
51	4	5.5	72	.66	57
50	2	8.5	64	.54	55
49	4	11.5	48	.42	54
48	1	14	44	.30	53
46	2	15.5	36	.06	51
45	1	17	32	−.05	49
42	3	19	20	−.41	46
38	1	21	16	−.89	41
34	1	22	12	−1.37	36
33	2	23.5	4	−1.42	36
28	1	25	0	−2.09	29
	25				

* Standard Deviation.

(The procedure used to obtain the percentile ranks in Table 4 is suggested for practical use. It gives the percentile rank of the lower limit of each score interval. However, if the score is taken as a point on the score scale, the percentile rank is based on a consideration that half of the cases at the score fall below it. When this procedure is followed no student in the group used to establish the percentile ranks can have a percentile rank as low as 0 or as high as 100.)

Percentile ranks have some of the same limitations as those mentioned above for ranks, since they merely provide information on the ordering of the individuals in a given group. Percentile ranks should not be added together or averaged. If the only use a teacher wants to make of derived scores is to record the ordering of students on a test, this can be done with ranks or percentile ranks.

A type of derived score that retains more than the ordinal information of ranks and percentile ranks is the standard score. Standard scores take into account the difference between and the ordering of raw scores. A student's standard score tells how many standard deviations his score is above or below the mean. A standard score for a student is obtained by subtracting the mean from his score and dividing the difference by the standard deviation. Carrying out this transformation for each student's score gives a set of standard scores with a mean of 0 and a standard deviation of 1; these are called z-scores. Thus in the distribution in Table 4, where the mean is 45.46 and the standard deviation is 8.37, the student with a raw score of 52 has a z-score of .78 since a score of 52 is .78 standard deviations above the mean. One student in this group has a z-score of $-.89$; his score, therefore, is .89 standard deviations below the mean of the group.

It is readily noted that z-scores involve the use of negative values and decimals. Other sets of standard scores that avoid these two characteristics of z-scores can be established. A set of standard scores with any desired mean and standard deviation can be obtained by the linear transformation $az + b$, where b is the desired mean and a is the desired standard deviation. It is often convenient to establish standard scores with a mean of 50 and a standard deviation of 10, as in the distribution in Table 4. Thus the person who has a raw score of 52 and a z-score of .78 has a standard score of 58 $(10 \times .78 + 50)$. One of the students has a standard score of 41 in this set; his score is 9/10 of a standard deviation below the mean of the group.

Any linear transformation of z-scores of the type discussed above will lead to a set of derived scores that are standard scores. They are derived scores because they provide information about a student's performance on the basis of the performance of others; they are standard scores because they provide this information in terms of the number of standard deviations the student's raw score is above or below the mean.

There are two basic advantages of standard scores over percentile ranks. First, they preserve the shape of the distribution of raw scores. If the raw scores are asymmetrical, the standard scores will be asymmetrical in exactly the same way. Second, standard scores are additive. If a student has a series of standard scores that are based on the same class or group of students, these scores may be weighted in any way, or averaged, to obtain an overall summary of his performance on the different tests.

Often teachers are tempted to avoid the use of derived scores owing to a fear that their use will lower standards. Both raw scores and derived scores provide information concerning what the student *did* on a test. Standards indicate what a student *should do* on a test and thus require a value judgment. The establishment of standards would require a value judgment with either raw scores or derived scores.

So far we have been considering the information from test scores. A study of a student's individual item responses yields additional information. But individual item responses must always be interpreted with caution, since information based on small samples of behavior may be unreliable and misleading. The analysis of a student's item responses may be used to indicate where more reliable information may profitably be sought, but this information should never be taken at face value.

A simple charting of responses is useful in studying the responses of individual students to different items as well as the pattern of group responses for each item. The procedure illustrated in Table 5 is simple and convenient. Ordering the papers on the basis of total scores and marking wrong responses reduces the work. With a simple check we indicate a wrong response to a computation, completion, or true-false item (items 1 through 10); and we write the letter of the wrong alternative selected for a multiple-choice item (items 11 through 20).

The teacher who charted the responses given in Table 5 can learn a number of things worthy of note. Considering the individual patterns of responses, for example, we find that even though students E.G. and T.S. had identical total scores (14), there is only one item that they both missed. E.G. had considerable trouble with the objectives sampled by the multiple-choice items, while T.S. had all of these right. Looking at the pattern of responses to individual items, we note among other things that item 7 was very difficult for the group, but the three who did get it right are all in the upper half of the distribution; four of the students with relatively high scores picked response D for item 19, but only one student with a low score picked this response. This line of analysis can yield valuable information about the test.

Information About the Test

Test results may be analyzed to answer questions about individual items and about the total test. It will be recalled that the main purpose of any test item is to tell us which students can exhibit the behaviors taught for (the Cans), and which students cannot exhibit these

TABLE 5

RESPONSES OF 16 STUDENTS TO ITEMS IN A 20-ITEM TEST*

Item	R.K.	G.T.	H.K.	B.B.	R.P.	S.A.	M.S.	R.M.	E.G.	T.S.	H.H.	M.T.	F.D.	R.D.	J.B.	D.E.	Number Right	Percent Right
1																	16	100
2					✓					✓						✓	13	81
3			✓												✓		14	88
4						✓				✓				✓	✓		12	75
5			✓													✓	14	88
6		✓								✓			✓	✓		✓	11	69
7				✓	✓	✓	✓	✓	✓	✓	✓	✓	✓	✓	✓	✓	3	19
8					✓		✓			✓	✓					✓	11	69
9								✓		✓		✓		✓		✓	11	69
10				✓		✓					✓	✓	✓	✓		✓	9	56
11															A		15	94
12					D				B		B			D		D	11	69
13													A	C	A		13	81
14																	16	100
15							A	B	B			B	B		B	B	9	56
16						C							C			D	13	81
17				B			B	A	A		A	B	A		B	A	7	44
18												B			D	B	13	81
19				D	D	D	D		C		C		A	C	D	C	6	38
20		D						A	A		C	C			C	No Res.	9	56
Score	20	18	18	16	15	15	15	15	14	14	13	13	12	12	10	6		

* A blank space indicates the right answer was given; a checkmark indicates the wrong answer was given; and the letters represent wrong

behaviors (the Cannots). In our discussion of item construction we made the point that the wording of an item or any aspect of the way it is presented to the students that leads the Cannots to get the item right or the Cans to get the item wrong results in false information from the item. To evaluate the item requires that the Cans and the Cannots be identified on some basis other than the item results alone.

To identify Cans and Cannots for most situations, it would be desirable to have completely external criteria, but generally such criteria are not readily available to teachers. Therefore a somewhat less satisfactory but plausible criterion is often used, based on the following rationale: *This item is one sampling of the objectives covered by the whole test. If this item is getting at an aspect of the area covered by the whole test, then it is reasonable to believe that people who do well on the whole test are those who should get the item right, and those who do poorly on the test should get the item wrong.* On this basis it is common practice to evaluate items in terms of the extent to which the high scorers (call them the Cans) get the item right and the low scorers (call them the Cannots) get the item wrong.

In separating the class into Cans and Cannots for item evaluation, the median may be used for groups of the size found in most classrooms. The students scoring above the median are labeled the Cans and the students scoring below the median are labeled the Cannots. Where larger groups are involved it is desirable to exclude the middle of the distribution, using the top one-fourth, 27 percent, or one-third of the group as the Cans and the lowest one-fourth, 27 percent, or one-third, correspondingly, as the Cannots. An expedient procedure for cumulating student responses for analysis is to separate the papers of the Can group from those of the Cannot group and tally the wrong responses and omits for each group. The number of right responses for each group may then be obtained by subtraction. Since most items used on classroom tests are missed by fewer than half the students, tallying is held to a minimum with this procedure.

The item analysis data tells us the extent to which the item differentiates between the Cans and the Cannots. If more Cans than Cannots answer the item correctly, the item is working in the desired direction and is called a positive discriminator. If more Cannots than Cans get the item right, the item is working against the test as a whole and is called a negative discriminator. The best items are generally considered to be those positive discriminators with the greatest spread between the number of Cans and the number of Cannots having right answers.

The item analysis data also tells us something about the difficulty of the items. The difficulty index, *p,* of an item is defined as the per-cent of a total group getting the item right (see Table 5); *p* shows the extent to which the group as a whole was successful on the item. The use to be made of test results will in part determine the difficulty level desired. In attempting to obtain a distribution of scores to determine the level of achievement of students in a class, it is generally desirable to have some relatively easy and also some relatively difficult items, with most items having indexes that center on the .50 to .60 range.

The item analysis data also gives us information concerning the effectiveness of the distractors in multiple-choice items. Distractors are put into multiple-choice items in an attempt to distract the Cannots, but not the Cans, from the right (or best) answer. A comparison of the number of Cannots who pick a distractor with the number of Cans selecting it indicates how well a distractor is working.

Let us consider the results of four items taken from a 26-item test on surfaces and volumes. The test, composed of 10 completion items and 16 multiple-choice items, was administered to a class of 32 students.

ITEM 3.   The label on a jar covers the area called the_____.

	Right Answer	Wrong Answer	Omit	Difficulty Index (*p*)
Cans	14	11	0	.75
Cannots	10	~~THL~~	1	

Two of the 16 Cans and five of the 16 Cannots got this item wrong, with one Cannot omitting the item. Thus 14 of the Cans and 10 of the Cannots got the item right. This item is a positive discriminator and is working, in degree, the way it should. Since 75 percent of the class an-swered correctly, it was not a very difficult item for the group. On the basis of this information the item would be worth using without revision for a similar group.

ITEM 4.   In the expression πr^2, the r^2 means the same as_____.

	Right Answer	Wrong Answer	Omit	Difficulty Index (*p*)
Cans	13	11	1	.88
Cannots	15	1	0	

On this item, 15 of the Cannots but only 13 of the Cans gave the keyed answer ($r \times r$). Thus it is a negative discriminator and should be altered if it is to be used again with a similar group. The difficulty index of .88 indicates that it was a fairly easy item for this group.

ITEM 16.   A solid having four faces would be a
           (A) Cube (B) Square (C) Pyramid (D) Prism

	A	B	C	D	Omit	Difficulty Index (p)
Cans	II	II	12	0	0	.50
Cannots	II	7HL II	4	III	0	

This item is doing as much as can be asked of it. A much larger number of Cans than Cannots got it right. Distractors B and D are working in the right direction. Even though distractor A attracted as many Cans as Cannots, the item is probably worth trying again as it stands.

ITEM 18.   How many formulas must be used to find the
           area of the figure shown?
           (A) one   (B) two   (C) three   (D) four

	A	B	C	D	Omit	Difficulty Index (p)
Cans	0	IIII	7HL III	4	0	.25
Cannots	0	7HL I	7HL I	4	0	

This item just did not work! The teacher had keyed the item D, and the same number of Cans and Cannots marked this alternative. The keyed answer was selected by the number that would be expected to select it by chance alone. Distractor A contributed nothing to the item, attracting neither Cannots nor Cans. Distractor B worked to a degree the way a distractor should work, drawing more Cannots than Cans. Distractor C was selected by two more Cans than Cannots, and by twice as many Cans as selected the keyed answer. The teacher should probably attempt in some other way to get at the objective he tried to sample with this item.

Item analysis data obtained from one group of students may be used in making judgments about the possible value of the item for use with another group of students. Any decisions on the use or revision of an item must be made on the basis that the next group of students to be presented with the item is similar to the group whose results were used in the item analysis. If the responses of a small group were used for the item analysis, the teacher may decide to withhold revision until he can get more information. A card file may be used to cumulate information on items. Each item used is put on a card and filed under the objective it samples. Every time an item is used the difficulty index is recorded, along with information on how the item discriminated and how the distractors worked (for multiple-choice items). When new or revised items are tried they may be added to the file, and the teacher builds up a collection of items on the objectives for which he teaches. He may then use this collection of tried items for making up tests without giving the same test again and again.

In addition to information about individual items, results of a test also provide information about its reliability, the consistency with which it measures. Reliability information is usually summarized in a reliability coefficient. Many procedures have been proposed for obtaining reliability coefficients. Two related procedures, based on a single administration of a test, require little more than the statistics already discussed. These procedures were developed by Kuder and Richardson (1).

The most widely used of the Kuder-Richardson procedures is expressed by the formula:

$$r_{11} = \frac{n}{n-1} \left[1 - \frac{\sum_{i=1}^{n} p_i q_i}{s^2} \right]$$

where n is the number of items on the test, s is the standard deviation of the raw scores, p_i is the percent of the group passing the ith item (the difficulty index obtained in the item analysis), and q_i is the percent of the group failing the ith item $(1 - p_i)$. To find the reliability coefficient by this procedure requires finding p, q, and the product pq for each item. The sum of these products is then substituted in the formula along with the standard deviation and the number of items to obtain a reliability coefficient.

The second Kuder-Richardson procedure involves somewhat less computation and gives a coefficient that is generally a reasonable approximation of that given by the procedure described above. This second procedure is expressed in the formula:

$$r_{11} = \frac{n}{n-1} \left[1 - \frac{M\left(1 - \frac{M}{n}\right)}{s^2} \right]$$

where M is the mean of the scores, n is the number of items and s is the standard deviation of the scores. This procedure may be used to obtain an estimate of the reliability of a test using only the mean and standard deviation of the raw scores and n, the number of items. Using this formula, we find that a 50-item test with a mean of 30 and a standard deviation of 6 has the reliability coefficient:

$$r_{11} = \frac{50}{49} \left[1 - \frac{30\left(1 - \frac{30}{50}\right)}{36} \right] = .68$$

Now let us consider the limitations of the two Kuder-Richardson procedures. Both give spuriously high coefficients for speeded tests and should not be used when time is a factor in determining the performance of the student. The formulas are set up for use with tests that are scored 1 for the right answer and 0 for a wrong answer to each item. If the scores are based on a constant weighting for the items (say 3 points for a correct answer and 0 for a wrong answer), the mean and standard deviation should both be divided by the weight prior to substitution in the formula. There are, however, other procedures that are not limited by the differential scoring of items (6).

Reliability coefficients are also obtained by computing correlation coefficients between half scores, between results of repeated administration of the same test, or between equivalent forms.

After a reliability coefficient for a test is obtained there remains the problem of interpretation. It may be said in general that the higher the reliability coefficient the better. Reliability coefficients fall between the limits 0.00 and 1.00. The more reliable a test, the closer the reliability coefficient will be to 1.00. On standardized achievement tests reliability coefficients generally are found to be somewhat above .75, many being above .90. From time to time attempts have been made to set minimal reliability coefficients. It is reasonable to expect that a teacher will use the most reliable information he can obtain (without sacrificing a disproportionate amount of relevance and objectivity), regardless of the absolute size of the reliability coefficient. But if a test with low absolute reliability is used, the probability of a sizable number of large errors must be recognized. The size of such errors is usually estimated by the standard error of measurement.

The probability of errors of different magnitudes may be estimated with the standard error of measurement, which is defined by the formula:

$$\text{Standard Error of Measurement} = s\sqrt{1 - r_{11}}$$

where s is the standard deviation and r_{11} is the reliability coefficient of the test, based on the scores of the students being tested or a comparable group. Based on the assumption that errors of measurement are normally distributed, it may be said that the odds are about 2 to 1 that a student's obtained score on a given test is no more than one standard error of measurement from his true score, and about 19 to 1 that this difference is no more than two standard errors of measurement (7). Thus a small difference of a few score points between the scores of two students may reflect only the unreliability of the test. In such cases the conclusion that the student with the higher score has achieved more will often be wrong.

Suppose that a certain test has a standard deviation (s) of 6 and a reliability coefficient (r_{11}) of .75. Then the standard error of measurement is $6\sqrt{1 - .75} = 3$. If John has a score of 68 on this test, the odds are about 2 to 1 that John's true score is included in the range 68 ± 3, or 65 to 71.

Any manipulation and interpretation of test scores involves assumptions. For example, calculation of the median, ranks, and percentile ranks assumes that test scores can be meaningfully ordered from lowest to highest; the calculation of the mean, standard deviation, and standard scores assumes, in addition, that we can meaningfully use the size of the differences between scores. A very good presentation of the assumptions underlying various statistics may be found in Siegal (4). Another possible source of information on these assumptions is a fellow faculty member who has studied statistics.

Summary

Procedures for the development of achievement tests and the interpretation of achievement test results are presented in this chapter. Course objectives stated in terms of student behavior are cited as the primary basis for achievement test construction. Specific procedures for the construction of achievement tests and the manipulation of test scores to provide information about the performance of a class, information about the performance of individual students, and information about the test itself are presented and discussed.

References

1. KUDER, G. FREDERIC, and RICHARDSON, M. W. "The Theory of Estimation of Test Reliability." *Psychometrika* 2: 151-60; 1937.

2. REMMERS, H. H., and GAGE, N. L. *Educational Measurement and Evaluation.* Revised edition. New York: Harper and Brothers, 1955.

3. Ross, C. C., and STANLEY, J. C. *Measurement in Today's Schools.* Third Edition. New York: Prentice-Hall, 1954.

4. SIEGEL, SIDNEY. *Nonparametric Statistics for the Behavioral Sciences.* New York: McGraw-Hill, 1956.

5. THOMAS, R. MURRAY. *Judging Student Progress.* New York: Longmans, Green and Co., 1954.
6. THORNDIKE, ROBERT L. "Reliability." *Educational Measurement.* Washington, D. C.: American Council on Education, 1951.
7. THORNDIKE, ROBERT L., and HAGEN, ELIZABETH. *Measurement and Evaluation.* New York: John Wiley and Sons, 1955.
8. TRAVERS, ROBERT M. W. *How to Make Achievement Tests.* New York: The Odyssey Press, 1950.

5

Analysis of Illustrative
Test Items

MAX A. SOBEL and DONOVAN A. JOHNSON

M AJOR EMPHASIS in evaluation is usually placed on the objectives of
instruction. Published tests, as well as teacher-made tests, frequently emphasize facts and skills to the neglect of other equally
important goals of instruction. Most mathematics teachers, however,
agree that it is important to teach for broader educational objectives in
mathematics and to measure what has been accomplished toward meeting these objectives. Therefore tests using a wide variety of items must
be developed and used in order to evaluate the many aspects of learning
in the classroom.

Preceding chapters have set forth basic principles for measurement
of achievement in mathematics and have offered specific suggestions
for procedure in constructing tests. In this chapter we shall attempt to
show how such ideas are used in the writing of items for a mathematics
achievement test and shall illustrate a variety of test items that measure
many phases of mathematics achievement, emphasizing different ways
to write a given test item. Each item will be analyzed to show the objective that it measures.

This chapter will not, however, endeavor to be a storehouse of items.
It will, instead, illustrate the varied types of items that can be devised
to sample student behavior. We cannot discuss all types of items or
items that measure all the objectives of mathematics instruction. We
hope the reader will perceive the variety of information one may obtain
by careful construction and judicious use of test items; he will then be
able to construct items that will measure achievement satisfactorily.

Objectives

Since objectives are of major importance in evaluation, let us take another look at them. Although we, as teachers of mathematics, aspire to achieve a wide variety of objectives, all too often we confine our measurement to those objectives we can most readily assess, such as acquisition of basic skills or facts. Important as skills and facts are, a study of mathematics should result in the achievement of much more. The professional literature cites such other desirable goals of instruction as the development of logical reasoning, creativeness, constructive attitudes, and good habits. The emphasis on understanding, reasoning, and problem solving in the emerging mathematics curriculum also shows the imperative need for the construction of new test items.

Many sets of objectives may be developed; there is, of course, no commonly accepted list. We hope that the reporting of our list here will not suggest that these objectives are official or complete or the best or the final ones. This, of course, is not the case. Objectives may vary from time to time and from school to school and from one mathematics course to another. However, in order to have a framework of reference, a sample list of objectives is presented below.

The student should:

—have a knowledge and understanding of mathematical processes, facts, and concepts;

—have skill in computing with understanding, accuracy, and efficiency;

—have the ability to use a general problem-solving technique;

—understand the logical structure of mathematics and the nature of proof;

—use mathematical concepts and processes to discover new generalizations and applications;

—recognize and appreciate the role of mathematics in society;

—develop study habits essential for independent progress in mathematics;

—develop reading skill and vocabulary essential for progress in mathematics;

—demonstrate such mental traits as creativity, imagination, curiosity, and visualization;

—develop attitudes that lead to appreciation, confidence, respect, initiative, and independence.

It may be possible, of course, to set up acceptable objectives that do not fall into any of the above categories. This list indicates the possibilities, however, and it should help us realize that teacher-made tests frequently sample only a very small portion of the outcomes one may expect from a study of mathematics. It is a major thesis of this chapter that if many objectives are accepted, then each one of them should be tested.

Certainly not all the aims of instruction in mathematics lend themselves to objective testing. Objectives dealing with attitudes, appreciations, and habits are probably best measured by such non-testing appraisal instruments as observations, projects, and reports. Such techniques are described in Chapter 7. The discussion here is limited to objectives that are usually measured by specific test items.

Teacher-Made or Published Tests?

When a decision is made to start a testing program, the question normally arises as to whether the teacher should use published tests or construct his own. There are many advantages in using published tests: They are prepared by experts in the field, they are usually easy to score and analyze, and the results obtained may be compared with nationally established norms. A complete discussion of available published evaluation materials, together with the advantages of using such instruments, will be found in Chapter 6.

Let us turn our attention, then, to teacher-made tests. What advantages warrant the time and energy necessary to prepare them? Among their many advantages over published tests are the following:

1. They may be adapted to the local situation—the teacher, the pupils, the community.

2. In these days of changing curricula, teacher-made tests are more easily kept up to date than published tests.

3. Test construction is often a real learning experience for the teacher.

4. Test construction may compel teachers to re-evaluate their objectives of instruction, a process which often leads to the improvement of such instruction.

With a little care teachers can invent test items that measure more than basic computational skills. The additional time for preparation of such tests or test items is rewarding in terms of the added information obtained about students' abilities in mathematics. Furthermore, such tests may inspire teachers to consider a wide variety of objectives of instruction. The experience of writing and analyzing tests should be part of every mathematics teacher's activities.

Illustrative Test Items

We do not favor any specific technique in writing items. Most teacher-made tests emphasize the subjective-type item, usually identified by such words as *solve, add, prove,* and *name.* These items are all too often evaluated in terms of the final answer produced, with scant attention given to the thought processes involved. Often, however, a great deal can be learned through the use of objective-type questions (multiple choice, matching, or true-false) that measure individual steps in a process. Furthermore, items of this type permit a much wider sampling of the knowledge and understanding possessed by a student than items in which a premium is placed only upon obtaining the correct answer to a problem.

The test items below are presented to help you recognize the wide range of abilities that can be measured. We shall attempt to illustrate various techniques for writing such items. It is not the purpose of this chapter, however, to provide a collection of tricky or unusual items, but rather to indicate the vast amount of information that may be obtained by careful construction of test items.

Although a single item may cover a number of objectives and sample a variety of difficulties, we do not attempt here to cover all possible objectives—an impossible task—or all areas of instruction. These items are intended to be illustrative only. They are placed in definite categories primarily for convenience.

Objective: The student should have skill in computing with understanding, accuracy, and efficiency.

We can test the accuracy and efficiency of a student's computational skill by asking him to complete a large number of problems in a limited amount of time. Such a collection of items generally does not provide adequate information as to the student's understanding of basic concepts and meanings. Nevertheless, most teacher-made tests are limited to items of this nature. Thus in elementary arithmetic we use such items as the following:

ITEM 1(a). Multiply:

$$\begin{array}{r} \$.21 \\ \times\ 34 \\ \hline \end{array}$$

By revising the form of this problem slightly, we can gain some additional insight into the student's understanding of the process involved.

ITEM 1(b). In the problem below, the numeral marked

(A) actually represents _____ × $.21

(B) actually represents _____ × $.21

(C) actually represents _____ × $.21

```
$ .21
 × 34
  ‾‾‾‾
   84   (A)
  630   (B)
  ‾‾‾‾
$7.14   (C)
```

Revising further, we combine both the preceding items in order to evaluate and encourage the student's thinking while he is demonstrating skills.

ITEM 1(c). Find the product of the numbers below. Then fill in the blanks to show the full meaning of the partial products.

```
$.21
× 34
‾‾‾‾
      =   4 × $.21 = _____
____  = __ × $.21 = _____
      = __ × $.21 = _____
```

Item 1(c) certainly measures whatever Item 1(a) measures, but it also provides the teacher with information that should enable him to distinguish between those who have learned by rote and those who understand the process. If acquisition of concepts is an important goal of instruction, then items must be devised to evaluate the formation of such concepts.

Following is an item that illustrates the use of addition properties in a unique situation. The emphasis is on the operation rather than on the sum.

ITEM 2. If we use Roman numerals, we have XV + VI = X + V + V + I = X + (V + V) + I = X + X + I = XXI. Which of the following properties are illustrated?

    I. Commutative property for addition
   II. Associative property for addition
  III. Distributive property for addition

    A. None   D. I and II only
    B. I only   E. I, II, and III
    C. II only

Objective: The student should have an understanding of mathematical processes and concepts.

ITEM 1. Which one of the following measurements has the greatest precision?

A.	3⅕ inches	D.	3¾ inches
B.	3⅔ inches	E.	3⁴⁄₇ inches
C.	3⅝ inches		

This item clearly illustrates how choices are written. Since precision of measurement is indicated by the size of the unit of measure, the correct choice is E. Note how the numerators and denominators are associated; one certainly would not want to associate the largest or the smallest numerator with the largest or smallest denominator. To do so would obscure the basis on which the most precise measurement is chosen. The choices are not arranged in order of precision, and the "3" and "inches" are constant so that they will be ruled out of the consideration.

Many concepts about functions, usually taught in high school, are important for both theoretical and computational reasons. Although there is a tendency to present at least a portion of the theory first in order to promote understanding, we often emphasize the applied aspects to the neglect of the theory. In many cases this practice may be pedagogically or mathematically wrong. If so, the kind of testing we do may confirm or correct the error of our ways. This may be the case with the logarithmic and trigonometric functions. Following is a common type of test question during a logarithm unit:

ITEM 2(a). Solve the following by using logarithms:

$$\frac{27 \times \sqrt{229}}{130}.$$

Since the students should know how to do this, such questions need to be asked. But it would be easy to convert the question into one that would emphasize some of the theory. For example:

ITEM 2(b). In computing

$$x = \frac{27 \times \sqrt{229}}{130},$$

we obtain $\log x = 7.5000 - 10$ in our next to last step. Without using tables, discuss whether the work so far is approximately correct. Give your reasons for believing it correct or incorrect, arguing in terms of both characteristic and mantissa.

This is an essay question, of course, with all the attendant difficulties of scoring. The scorer must have the desired answer in mind in all its detail, and the student must be trained to answer in appropriate detail. But the question may be phrased for objective scoring as follows:

ITEM 2(c): Consider

$$a = \frac{27 \times \sqrt{229}}{130}.$$

Without using tables, estimate which of the following is most nearly correct in the next to last step of the computation.

(A) 7.4500 − 10   (D) 0.4500
(B) 7.5000 − 10   (E) 0.5000
(C) 0.3000

These choices may be altered to make an easier or harder item, or an item emphasizing only characteristic or mantissa.

Following are other multiple-choice items which tend to emphasize the theory rather than the computational aspects of logarithmic functions:

ITEM 3. What is the logarithm of 2 to the base four?

(A) 0.5   (D) 8
(B) 2   (E) Cannot be determined on the
(C) 4   basis of the given information

ITEM 4. If $\log_{10} 2 = 0.3010$, then $\log_{10} 5 = $ (?)

(A) 2.5×0.3010 (C) $2.5 + 0.3010$

(B) $\dfrac{0.3010}{2.5}$ (D) $1 - 0.3010$

                                    (E) None of these

ITEM 5. Which of the following is the smallest?

(A) $\log_{10} 2$ (D) $\log_5 5$
(B) $\log_{10} 5$ (E) $\log_2 2$
(C) $\log_5 2$

ITEM 6. If $100^{100} = 10^x$, then $x = $ (?)

(A) 100   (D) 10,000
(B) 200   (E) 2^{100}
(C) 1000

Objective: The student should associate mathematical concepts with applications in community situations.

Item 1. Imagine you are living in a country with two political parties, and an election is coming up. There promises to be a violent campaign in which the OUT party will try to get into control of the government and the IN party will try to stay in control. Part of the campaign is about inflation and price control. The government has released figures to show the cost of living in 1960 compared with that of 10 years earlier (1950). Table A presents the official figures; Graph X has appeared in newspapers supporting one party; Graph Y, in newspapers supporting the other party.

Table A

Year	1950	1951	1952	1953	1954	1955	1956	1957	1958	1959	1960
Cost of Living (1950 prices = 100)	100	105	110	115	120	125	130	135	140	145	150

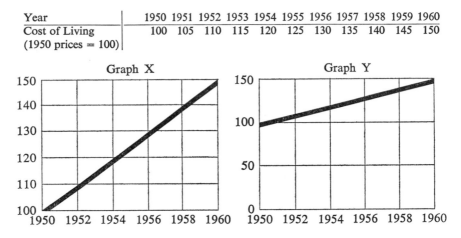

Refer each of the following statements to the above situation and graphs. Decide if it is true or false. If it is true, mark it plus (+); if false, mark it zero (0).

    1._____Both graphs present exactly the same data.

    2._____Both graphs present the same picture at a quick glance.

    3._____You can read the cost-of-living figures more accurately from Graph X.

    4._____Papers supporting the IN party would probably use graph X.

    5._____Papers supporting the OUT party would probably use graph X to emphasize the inflation problem.

    6._____A newspaper interested in presenting a true picture would probably use graph X.

This item, which may be varied to fit local situations, will test the student's ability to interpret a statistical graph correctly.

Objective: The student should have an understanding of our number system.

A major objective of instruction at almost all levels is to develop an understanding of our own number system. We evaluate learning in this area with test items that range from the simple to the sophisticated. Consider, for example, the following sequence, which is appropriate at a variety of grade levels, for testing the understanding of place value:

ITEM 1. Completion: The numeral 372 represents ___ hundreds, ___ tens, and ___ ones.

ITEM 2. True or False:

(a) The 4 in 428 is twice the value of the 2.

(b) The 3 in 357 stands for three hundreds.

(c) The whole number of tens in 6853 is 685.

(d) The 0 in 21.08 serves as a placeholder.

ITEM 3. Multiple Choice: In the number 842, the 8 has a value that is

(a) Twice the value of the 4.

(b) Four times the value of the 2.

(c) Twenty times the value of the 4.

(d) Forty times the value of the 2.

(e) Two hundred times the value of the 4.

Objective: The student should have an understanding of number systems with bases other than ten.

At a later stage of a student's development in mathematics we can test his understanding of the number system with items that use number bases other than ten. Consider the following:

ITEM 1. Imagine a place where the inhabitants have only 5 fingers, and numbers are written in groups of 5. Thus "23" would mean two groups of 5, and 3 units. What symbol would be used in such a system to represent the number of marks in the following set:

```
* * * * *        (a) 24
* * * * *        (b) 34
* * * * *        (c) 44
* * * * *        (d) 54
* * * *
```

Assuming no prior knowledge of a base five system of numeration, Item 1 serves not only to measure understanding of numeral systems but also to evaluate the student's ability to generalize.

To test understanding of groupings in various bases after presentation of such a unit, the following item may be appropriate:

ITEM 2. The number of x's in the accompanying figure is written below in numerals in four different bases. Which numerals are correct?

```
X   X   X   X
X   X   X   X
X   X   X   X
X   X
```

(I) 24 $_{\text{five}}$ (II) 14 $_{\text{seven}}$ (III) 12 $_{\text{twelve}}$ (IV) 1110 $_{\text{two}}$

(a) Only I is correct.

(b) II and III are correct.

(c) I, III, and IV are correct.

(d) All are correct.

Objective: The student should be stimulated to demonstrate creativeness and imagination.

Going a step further, the next item evaluates the student's creativeness and originality, as well as his ability to apply fundamental principles in new situations. This is by no means an easy item, and it would not normally be presented to a class until after a complete discussion of numeration systems.

ITEM 1.   Consider a number system where the following symbols are used:

$$\square \text{ is } 0$$
$$1 \text{ is } 1$$
$$V \text{ is } 2$$
$$\Delta \text{ is } 3$$

(a) Write the next three numbers in the sequence:

1, V, Δ, 1□, 11, 1V, 1Δ, V□, ——, ——, ——,

Find the:

(b) sum $V + \Delta =$ ——.

(c) product $V \times V =$ ——.

(d) quotient $V1 \div V =$ ——.

(e) difference $V\square - V =$ ——.

Objective: The student should understand the logical structure of mathematics and the nature of proof.

Developing the ability to think logically is an objective of almost every course in mathematics, although it receives greatest emphasis in the field of geometry. While it is frequently claimed that the study of mathematics should enable one to apply elements of reasoning in non-mathematical situations, few teachers of mathematics try to evaluate such outcomes of instruction because of the difficulty of finding suitable items.

The items that follow attempt to measure this important aspect of learning, using a variety of techniques.

ITEM 1. During a survey in a certain school it was found that some of the students cheat on exams. Assuming the conclusion to be valid, what can be said of the following inferences: (True—False—Indeterminate)?

1. Some students in the school cheat on exams.
2. Many students in the school cheat on exams.
3. All students in the school cheat on exams.
4. Some students in the school do not cheat on exams.
5. Most students in the school do not cheat on exams.
6. Some students who do not cheat on exams are in this school.

ITEM 2. Consider the statement: *Studying hard is a necessary condition for getting an A.* This is equivalent to which of the following:

I. If you study hard, then you will get an A.
II. If you get an A, then you have studied hard.
III. If you don't study hard, then you will not get an A.
IV. If you don't get an A, then you have not studied hard.

(a) only I
(b) only I and II
(c) only II
(d) only II and III
(e) I, II, III, and IV

It is quite common for a teacher to evaluate achievement in a geometry class with a test in which the student is required to complete a number of formal proofs. The ability to organize and present a deductive proof is, of course, important in this area. A student may have a considerable knowledge of geometry, however, but fail to produce the necessary proof. Through careful construction of objective test items, a teacher may be able to obtain a great deal of information concerning the student's knowledge of the nature of proof as well as his ability to detect errors in logic. Consider, for example, the following items:

ITEM 3. If perpendiculars, *WY* and *WR*, are drawn to two radii, *XZ* and *XS*, from the midpoint, *W*, of the arc intercepted by the radii, the perpendiculars are equal. Which statement in the following proof is wrong or of no value?

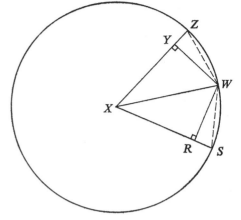

    1. $\angle ZXW = \angle SXW$

    2. $XW = XW$

    3. $\triangle XZW \cong \triangle XWS$

    4. Two right triangles are congruent if the hypotenuse and acute angle of one equals the hypotenuse and acute angle of the other.

ITEM 4. In each of the following examples indicate whether the conclusion has been logically drawn from the premises. Assume the premises to be true. If the syllogism is not valid, state what error in reasoning has been made.

    1. If a radius is perpendicular to a chord, then it bisects the chord.
       AB bisects the chord *CD* in circle *O*.
       Hence, *AB* is a radius of the circle *O*.

    2. If *p* implies *q*, then *a* implies *b*.
       However, *a* does not imply *b*.
       Hence, *p* does not imply *q*.

ITEM 5. In proving the theorem, "Two tangents to a circle from an external point are equal," two triangles are proved congruent by showing that they have respectively equal which of the following parts?

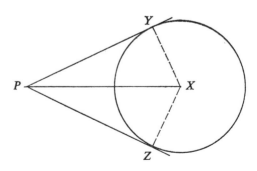

    (a) three sides

    (b) two sides and the included angle

    (c) two angles and the included side

    (d) the hypotenuse and one side

Objective: The student should have a knowledge and understanding of mathematical processes, facts, and concepts.

Much time in algebra courses is devoted to teaching students to draw and interpret graphs. Typical test items for such a unit may be:

ITEM 1. Graph $y = 2x - 1$ showing the x and y intercepts.

ITEM 2. Graph $x + y = 2$ and $2x - y = 5$ on the same set of axes showing their point of intersection.

Important as such items are, they do not supply us with sufficient information. A student may draw a graph incorrectly, but know a great deal that is not revealed to the teacher. The following item demonstrates how one may obtain a greater variety of easily scorable information in a relatively short period of time.

ITEM 3. Study the following graph. Then answer the questions, all of which refer to this graph.

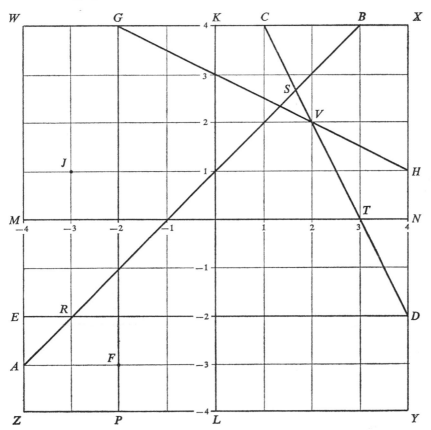

A. Each pair of letters at the right indicates a line on the graph. Complete
   the following with choices made from this list.

1. The x-axis is the line ———.	*KL*	*YZ*
2. The y-axis is the line ———.	*MN*	*XY*
3. The graph of $y = -2$ is ———.	*AB*	*WZ*
4. The graph of $y = x + 1$ is ———.	*CD*	*GP*
5. The graph of $y + 2x = 6$ is———.	*ED*	*GH*
6. The graph of $x = 0$ is ———.	*WX*	
7. The graph of $x + 2y = 6$ is———.		

B. Find the following values from the graph:

   8. The coordinates of *J* are   ———.
   9. The abscissa of *V* is   ———.
   10. The ordinate of *F* is   ———.
   11. The slope of *AB* is   ———.
   12. The y-intercept of *AB* is ———.
   13. The x-intercept of *CD* is ———.
   14. The slope of a line drawn through *J* parallel to *CD* would
       be   ———.
   15. The slope of *ED* is   ———.

C. Mark the following true or false:

   16. Both the abscissa and ordinate of point *R* are negative. ———.
   17. Line *KL* has a slope of zero.   ———.
   18. Lines *MN* and *ED* have the same slope.   ———.
   19. A line through *F*, parallel to *AB*, would have the same y-intercept
       as *AB*.   ———.
   20. A line through *J* and *T* would have the same x-intercept as
       CD.   ———.

The student is not asked to construct a graph, and this item does
not give information about his ability to construct his own graph.
However, the teacher can obtain more information for evaluating the
student's fund of knowledge of graphing through such items than by
having him do actual graphing.

Objective: The student should have the ability to perform geometric constructions.

Evaluation of learnings in the area of geometric construction is usually
a difficult task. Typically we ask the student to perform an actual construction:

ITEM 1. From an external point P, construct a tangent to a circle O.

The teacher then must examine the construction as well as the student's discussion and proof. This is a valuable type of exercise for the student, but only a relatively few such time-consuming items may be placed on any test. By modifying the item we can get at the same information in a much shorter period of time and in more easily scorable form. For example:

ITEM 2. From an external point P, a tangent to the circle O has been constructed. Which of the following groups of letters show the order in which the lines they represent were drawn:

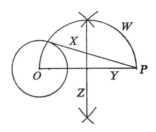

    (a) *XYZW*

    (b) *YZWX*

    (c) *YWZX*

    (d) *XZYW*

Objective: The student should have the vocabulary and reading skill essential for progress in mathematics.

Acquisition of basic facts and vocabulary is another objective in the teaching of geometry. We may test a student's knowledge of basic definitions quite readily with an item that merely asks for such a definition.

ITEM 1. Define a regular pyramid.

On the other hand, repetition by the student of the words that define this object does not necessarily present a complete picture of his understanding of the properties of a regular pyramid. We may get at the latter by means of a true-false item which requires more than mere recall of a definition.

ITEM 2. Place a plus sign before each item that completes a true statement. Place a zero before each one that completes a false statement. Each completion must be judged on its own merits and answered separately.

A regular pyramid has:

    ————1. all edges equal.

    ————2. an altitude that passes through the intersection of the medians of the base if the pyramid is triangular.

    ————3. an altitude less than any edge.

    ————4. congruent isosceles triangles for lateral faces.

    ————5. four equal faces if it is triangular.

Objective: The student should be stimulated to demonstrate such mental activities as visualization.

Throughout the study of mathematics we encourage our students to try to visualize the problems they encounter. Thus we suggest that they draw sketches in geometry as an aid to thinking, and draw diagrams in algebra to help solve verbal problems. We can encourage them further in attempts at visualization if we include in our tests such items as the following:

ITEM 1. The line given for each example below is $2\frac{1}{2}$ inches long. Show how you can get the answers to these examples by dividing the lines into fractional parts. Label your diagram, so that the process is explained.

A. $1\frac{1}{4} + 1\frac{1}{4} = 2\frac{1}{2}$

B. $2\frac{1}{2} - \frac{3}{4} = 1\frac{3}{4}$

C. $\frac{1}{2} \times 5 = 2\frac{1}{2}$

D. $2\frac{1}{2} \div \frac{1}{4} = 10$

ITEM 2. The rectangle below consists of a square of area 16 and another rectangle of area 12. What is the distance PQ?

(A) 3   (B) 4   (C) 5   (D) 6   (E) 7

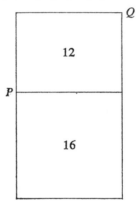

ITEM 3. What is the area of the shaded section of this rectangle?

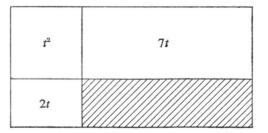

ITEM 4. Write a formula in factored form for the shaded area of this figure.

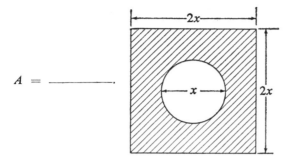

$A = \underline{\qquad}$.

ITEM 5. Label the four parts of this rectangle to show the partial products of $(x + 2)\,(x + 5)$.

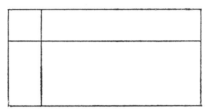

Objective: *The student should have the ability to use a general problem-solving technique.*

In a sense, almost all the work we do in mathematics involves problem solving of one type or another. In our testing program we invariably present students with problems to solve. But we frequently fail to gather adequate information on the problem-solving processes, which would enable us to guide the student in his future efforts. In the items that follow the student is not required to solve completely any single problem. Rather he is asked to answer questions that should reveal a great deal of information concerning various phases of his thinking process as he attempts to solve problems.

ITEM 1. To the right are several algebraic expressions in which n represents a number. Choose the one that best represents each English statement and write the letter of your choice in the space provided.

_____ half of the number	A. $2n$	F. $2 - n$
_____ the square of the number	B. $n + 2$	G. n^2
_____ the sum of the number and two	C. $n - 2$	H. $n + \frac{1}{2}$
_____ twice the number	D. $n = 2$	I. $n - \frac{1}{2}$
_____ two divided by the number	E. $n/2$	J. not given
_____ two is the number		
_____ two less than the number		

ITEM 2. Write the required algebraic expressions in the spaces provided. (Do not make equations, as insufficient information is given.)

A father is nine times as old as his son. If the son is now n years old,

        What is the father's age?   _____

        How old will the son be in 8 years?   _____

        How old will the father be then?   _____

One satellite travels s miles per hour; another goes faster by 750 miles per hour.

        How far will the slow satellite go in two hours?   _____

        What is the speed of the fast satellite?   _____

        How far does the fast satellite go in two hours?   _____

ITEM 3. From the problem, table, and diagram below decide whether each of the following equations is true. If it is true, mark plus ($+$) before it; if it is not true, mark zero (0) before it.

"Two friends, Bill and Joe, live in towns M miles apart. Deciding to meet at the earliest possible time, they leave their own homes at the same time and drive toward each other. Bill travels b miles per hour and Joe travels y miles per hour. How long will it take them to meet?"

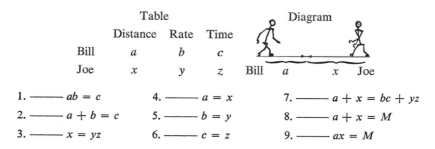

	Table		
	Distance	Rate	Time
Bill	a	b	c
Joe	x	y	z

Diagram — Bill a x Joe

1. ____ $ab = c$ 4. ____ $a = x$ 7. ____ $a + x = bc + yz$

2. ____ $a + b = c$ 5. ____ $b = y$ 8. ____ $a + x = M$

3. ____ $x = yz$ 6. ____ $c = z$ 9. ____ $ax = M$

ITEM 4. A marble is shot vertically upward with an initial velocity of 448 feet per second. At the end of the first second, the velocity is 416 feet per second. At the end of two seconds, the velocity is 384 feet per second. In how many seconds will the marble stop ascending and start to descend?

   1. Is this situation an example of an arithmetic or geometric progression?   _____

   2. What is the first term of the progression?   _____

   3. What is the last term of the progression?   _____

   4. What formula should be used to find the time the marble reaches maximum height?   _____

   5. How many seconds did it take until the marble started to descend?   _____

Objective: The student should use mathematical concepts to discover new generalizations or applications.

One means of evaluating this objective is the performance test, in which students are given materials and are asked to use them to discover relationships or solve problems. Most modern curricula emphasize the importance of discovery in learning new ideas and principles in mathematics. If this is an important phase of mathematics instruction, then it is altogether reasonable that tests should be developed that measure the student's ability to discover.

A performance test measures application and originality rather than memorized facts and skills. The student is presented with a situation different from the textbook description, and he must apply or transfer his knowledge to this new situation.

ITEM 1. At this station you are given some sheets of paper. Each one is to be folded to illustrate a relationship between certain lines. The lines are the creases made by folding the paper. It is assumed that a crease formed by folding a paper is a straight line. It is also assumed that a crease will pass through a given point. In addition, it is assumed that a fold can be made so that one crease falls upon another.

Materials: Wax paper of irregular shape, yellow paper triangle, section of red paper circle.

Fold each sheet according to the following directions:

1. Fold the wax paper to form three parallel creases.
2. Fold the yellow triangle so that a crease forms an altitude from one vertex to the opposite side. Fold all three altitudes to see if they intersect in a point.
3. Locate the center of the red circle by the intersection of two creases.

The purpose of this item is to discover or illustrate the following geometric relations by use of paper folding:

a. Lines perpendicular to the same line are parallel.
b. The altitudes of a triangle are concurrent.
c. The center of a circle is the point of intersection of the perpendicular bisectors of any two chords.

Objective: The student should use mathematical concepts to discover new generalizations or applications.

"Every teacher is a reading teacher" is an often-repeated statement. Certainly teachers of mathematics will agree that reading is an important phase of learning and that a conscious effort must be made to teach youngsters how to read mathematical literature. Frequently the major difficulty that students encounter in problem solving is related to reading. We can offer specific instruction in reading and evaluate such instruction in a variety of ways. One means is to present a test to determine the student's ability to read and comprehend new material.

ITEM 1. Read the following two paragraphs. Then select the best answer to each of the five questions which follow. You may refer back to the written material if necessary.

A number that has been of great interest to mathematicians is a prime number. A whole number greater than one is called a prime number if it can be divided evenly only by itself and one. The smallest prime numbers are 2, 3, 5, 7, 11, and 13. The number 1 might be considered prime, but this is not the custom. To do so would force us to state exceptions to many statements about prime numbers. For this reason 2 is considered the smallest prime number. Information about prime numbers is important because they are the building blocks of all numbers. Many statements in the study of numbers are based on whether or not a number is prime. More than 2000 years ago Euclid, who is most famous for his book on geometry, proved that the number of primes is infinite.

Another interesting group of numbers has been named perfect numbers. These numbers are the whole numbers which are exactly equal to the sum of all their divisors except themselves. The smallest perfect number is 6, for the divisors of 6 are 1, 2, and 3, and $6 = 1 + 2 + 3$. Some numbers, such as 10, have divisors that add to less than themselves: $5 + 2 + 1 = 8$. These integers are called deficient numbers. Some numbers, like 12, are called excess numbers because the sum of the divisors is more than themselves.

1. Which one of the following is a prime number?

    A. 51

    B. 55

    C. 57

    D. 59

2. Which one of the following is a perfect number?

    A. 12

    B. 20

    C. 28

    D. 36

3. Which one of the following is a deficient number?

    A. 2

    B. 6

    C. 18

    D. 24

4. What is the number of even primes?

   A. infinite

   B. unknown

   C. equal to the number of odd primes

   D. one

5. Which one of the following statements is true?

   A. The decimal .6 is a perfect number since $.1 + .2 + .3 = .6$.

   B. The decimal .5 is a prime number.

   C. The number 36 is an excess number.

   D. The smallest prime number is 1.

Summary

Most teachers of mathematics will agree that there are many outcomes that may be expected from a study of mathematics. It has been the point of view of this chapter that if such a wide range of objectives exists, then evaluation of these should take place.

Typical teacher-made tests fail to gather the quantity of information one really should possess to have a complete picture of a student's knowledge on any particular subject. They tend to place a premium on reproduction of definitions, presentation of proofs, or obtaining the correct solution to computational exercises.

We have tried, in this chapter, to present a collection of test items indicating the wide variety of information that may be obtained by careful test construction. Multiple-choice, true-false, completion, and matching items are easy to score, and may provide the teacher with a far more complete picture of the understanding and knowledge possessed by a student than subjective items.

The specific items that have been presented are not to be taken as models, but should indicate what can be done if time is given to this all-important process of evaluation. We hope that you will now attempt to construct test items that measure, as completely as possible, the learning that has taken place for a particular unit. Teachers of mathematics, who insist upon so many claims for their subject, should make certain that sufficient time and care is devoted to this all-important process of evaluation.

6

Published Evaluation Materials

SHELDON S. MYERS

THE SELECTION of appropriate evaluation instruments in mathematics is as important and as demanding a responsibility for the teacher and administrator as the selection of textbooks. Because of the wide range in quality and type of available published mathematics tests, the task of selection is not easy. In some cases selection is impossible because no appropriate instrument is available for the purpose in mind. In this era, when the mathematics curriculum is undergoing such extensive revision, the selection of appropriate evaluation instruments is becoming increasingly difficult and, at the same time, increasingly important. There is a growing urgency to develop new mathematics tests to meet the measurement needs of the future and to provide one of the means for judging results of new programs.

This chapter will attempt to help you in the selection of mathematics tests by discussing general procedures of selection, surveying the types of tests available, discussing the value of published testing materials, presenting criteria and techniques for the selection of mathematics tests, and providing an annotated bibliography of recent mathematics tests (see Appendix).

Selection Procedures

How should a school proceed in its choice of a published mathematics test? It is quite clear that the teachers of the courses involved should make the final decision. This is not an isolated effort, however, and certain types of liaison must exist. Over-all coordination may be provided by the entire mathematics staff and the department chairman. The principal, the superintendent, or the supervisor in charge of guidance and testing should be kept informed of decisions, so as to provide a school-wide or system-wide overview. This is particularly important when test batteries cutting across subject areas are involved, and uniformity and comparability of scores and norms are relevant. At this point, plans should be made regarding the use and the central recording of test results. The teachers concerned should explore together the questions they wish to answer with the published tests they select. The school, through its library, should provide the staff with up-to-date literature about tests and their selection. Mathematics teachers should review their test selections annually to determine whether the tests selected in the past are still serving their purpose.

Types of Mathematics Tests Available

The types of mathematics tests may be classified by a number of more or less useful criteria. Titles of tests are often misleading, and one must always examine the content of a test before coming to any conclusion about its type or purpose. This is particularly true when the term *diagnostic* appears in the title. Often there is no distinction in content between a diagnostic test and a general achievement test in arithmetic. Tests may be classified by subject matter, by purpose, by format, and by grade level.

Classification by subject matter has usually involved the following categories: arithmetic (also general mathematics), algebra (beginning and advanced), geometry (plane and solid), trigonometry, analytic geometry, calculus, and general achievement. While general mathematics tests often involve some elementary algebra and geometry, they are for the most part tests of arithmetic, especially applied arithmetic. General achievement tests in mathematics, on the other hand, are usually samples of the traditional high school mathematics courses. Some modern curricular trends that break down the traditional mathematics compartments may tend to make the subject matter classification of mathematics tests less desirable.

Classification by purpose involves the following categories: achievement or survey, diagnostic, prognostic, and competitive or contest. Classification by format involves the following categories: objective, essay, and the research problem. Classification by grade level may involve discrete or fractional parts of grades, or groups, such as intermediate grades, primary grades, junior high school, senior high school.

It is usually helpful to consider more than one of these classifying dimensions (subject matter, purpose, format, grade level) when selecting a test. In this way a wider array of relevant factors enters the selection process. Since these classifying dimensions cut across one another, a two-way grid using two of the classifying dimensions may be used to identify individual tests and to show the quantities of the different kinds of tests available (see Table 1).

TABLE 1

NUMBER OF PUBLISHED MATHEMATICS TESTS AVAILABLE
IN THE UNITED STATES AS OF JANUARY 1960

Subject	Purpose			Total
	Survey	Diagnostic	Prognostic	
Arithmetic	37	10	2	49
Algebra	20	1	6	27
Geometry	18	1	3	22
Trigonometry	3	0	0	3
General Achievement	8	0	0	8
			Total	109

Source: These figures were compiled from the bulletin *Mathematics Tests Available in the United States,* published by the National Council of Teachers of Mathematics.

Table 1 shows a relative lack of diagnostic mathematics tests in subjects other than arithmetic; this is probably due to the difficulty of obtaining sufficient score units to yield a reliable measure in each component being diagnosed. If good tests of 40 to 50 minutes length are broken down into sections for diagnostic purposes, there will not be enough questions in each section to yield a score of sufficient reliability for accurate diagnosis. Even in arithmetic the analytical diagnostic tests require far more administrative time than the average classroom period. This does not mean that a teacher cannot derive valuable diagnostic information from survey achievement tests. The score is only one small part of the information that may be obtained from a good achievement test.

There are several procedures that may be helpful in obtaining information from a test. The teacher may learn much, for example, by examining the individual papers closely and studying the pattern of each pupil's responses. He may interview certain pupils after a test and have them explain the reasons for their answers. He may have the class as a whole discuss the problems and various solutions after a test has been administered; some tests are so rich and stimulating in content that this is a worthwhile educational experience as well as a measurement technique. If the teacher studies the pattern of right and wrong answers for an entire class, he may discover classwide misconceptions and lines of necessary class work for the future. In these procedures the emphasis should not be on coaching for a particular test or set of questions but on teaching important mathematical ideas and concepts to which certain tests or sets of questions serve merely as a springboard.

Although the use of machine answer sheets presents certain difficulties in carrying out the above procedures, many published tests facilitate such procedures by providing profiles of pupil performance on clusters of related questions, by identifying in interpretive manuals the questions measuring certain concepts, or by providing auxiliary tally and record sheets for this purpose. In some cases teachers may arrange with publishers to have answer sheets scored and analyzed at the same time. Diagnosis has many facets, and a good teacher should be alert for diagnostic information from many sources.

The most important question about prognostic tests is their validity, and the most important question about validity is the criterion. The criterion of an algebra aptitude or prognostic test is, presumably, success in a later course in algebra. Since teachers vary in their methods and goals, whose course shall be used for measuring validity? Even after this is decided arbitrarily by agreement, there is still a problem of measuring the criterion. In the case of the algebra prognostic test, are end-of-course grades, end-of-course achievement test scores, teacher judgments, or combinations of these to be used as measures of the criterion? Criterion measures are often less reliable than the predicting instrument, so that low validities are often not the fault of the predicting instrument. Research studies in validity are sometimes directed at improving the reliability of the criterion measures.

An important validity criterion of an achievement test in mathematics would be concerned with how well the test samples a specified universe of content. This is known as content validity. Predictive validity and content validity are two of the more important forms of validity known to specialists in measurement.

Reliability, on the other hand, is concerned with how consistently a test measures whatever it is supposed to measure. Predictive validity coefficients are often correlation coefficients between test scores and later course grades. Such coefficients will usually run in the region of .45 to .65. Good reliability coefficients will generally run higher than validity coefficients, in the range .80 to .95.

Since it is not always possible to express validity in the form of coefficients, the interpretive manual must be read carefully to find evidence about the validity of a test. This is especially important in considering the selection of a prognostic test. It would be wise for any teacher or school to select a prognostic test for a probationary period of three to four years. During this time the test grades earned by pupils may be compared with later grades earned in the subject being predicted. These grades may also be combined with end-of-course achievement test scores to improve the criterion measure.

One should remember that such predictive instruments do not, and cannot, measure with anything near micrometer precision. If prognostic test scores, when added to the previous record of a student, help to increase the teacher's ability to judge the student's capacity to profit by further instruction, this is about all that may be expected. One cannot expect to find a rigorous method of predicting successes and failures. In the current trend toward the careful selection of students for particular classes in mathematics, teachers should exercise three precautions:

1. Scores on tests used for grouping should be supplemented by as much additional information as possible, such as cumulative records and teacher judgments.
2. Grouping should be flexible, enabling pupils to move from one group to another in the light of performance.
3. Provision for individual differences is necessary, even in selected groups.

The objective-type item is the one most widely used in published mathematics tests because of the ease and objectivity of scoring, and the multiple choice item is the most common of the objective types. However, the objective item is not the only type used in large-scale testing programs. The essay question is used in the special competitions of the Mathematical Association of America, in special contests here and abroad, and in the College Entrance Examination Board's Advanced Placement Examination in Mathematics (30 objective and 10 essay questions). Reader reliability coefficients in essay test scoring can be raised to above .90 if care is taken beforehand to assure clear understanding of the grading criteria.

The grade level classification of mathematics tests applies mainly to arithmetic, although some general achievement tests in mathematics have been classified in this way. With the growth and spread of newer curricula in mathematics, grade level distinctions may become even less appropriate, especially after grade 8. Consequently it may become even more important for tests to measure insights and broad understandings, rather than specific grade-pitched skills. The chief value of grade level classification lies in making it easier to select tests of appropriate vocabulary and difficulty. Usually such tests come in batteries involving sequences of grades, and they yield scores in terms of grade placement. Two difficulties sometimes arise with such tests: (*a*) with superior classes they may hold up an inferior standard of performance, and (*b*) if norming is done at scattered points along the grade scale, the interpolated and extrapolated grade placement scores may have considerable statistical error and may therefore be quite unreliable.

The Values of Published Mathematics Tests

All published mathematics tests do not have the values discussed here. Such values may be lacking because of inferiority of a particular test or because of the user's lack of effort to realize them.

A good published test is usually the result of highly scientific construction involving advanced pretesting on appropriate populations; item analyses for discrimination and difficulty; extensive review and editing to produce terse, unambiguous phrasing; and meticulous scrutiny by mathematicians for soundness and national curricular appropriateness. An experienced test-maker must have highly developed writing skills; technical skill in test rationale, design, specifications, and construction; statistical judgment for interpreting item analyses; mathematical background; an understanding of the student; and up-to-date knowledge of the curriculum. A single 40-minute form of a mathematics test constructed with such resources would cost from $5,000 to $10,000 to produce. Schools may conserve their resources by buying suitable tests instead of becoming involved in the expensive job of developing them.

Published tests usually provide normative data for comparing the performances of individuals or classes with the mean performance of national and regional groups in the same subject or grade. Such comparisons are rough and approximate. There is a strong trend for schools and school systems to construct their own local norms to supplement national norms. More differentiated norms are likely to appear in conjunction with standardized tests of the future. Published tests are often suitable instruments of educational research because of the availability of regional or national norms and because of their statistical design and high reliability.

Teacher-made classroom tests should not be the only criterion for promotion or grading. Scores on published mathematics tests should provide part of the total evaluation information gathered by a teacher each year; this may protect pupils from inaccurate evaluation. Standardized test scores also enable one to judge the product of a variety of schools. This was one of the chief reasons for the establishment of the College Entrance Examination Board.

There is a widespread misconception that published objective tests are inherently limited to measuring only the discrete, factual aspects of courses, and that only the essay question can probe deeper. This is not true. Most of the mathematics tests being developed today require insight and originality in problem-solving behavior, rather than mere facts and manipulation. For this reason the taking of a good modern mathematics test can be a worthwhile learning experience for the student. Such tests can present the student with a model of correct and precise mathematical language and can strengthen his concepts by involving him in many rich and varied applications of mathematical principles. When mathematics tests are of this kind, then the best preparation for them is a number of years of good mathematics courses with homework conscientiously done, rather than a month or two of specific coaching.

Other notes of caution are in order. Testing is on the increase, with the assistance of federal funds and the proliferation of large-scale scholarship and college entrance testing programs. While teachers should consider the many possibilities of an improved testing program, they should also consider the real dangers of over-testing in the schools. These dangers may be reduced if schools develop system-wide testing programs that place controls on standardized testing and that contribute to the optimum utilization of test results. But a printed test, however well chosen, may not exactly measure the particular emphasis in a given class and therefore should be supplemented with teacher-made tests. Conversely, a teacher-made series of tests should be supplemented with published tests.

Criteria for Selecting a Published Mathematics Test

Usually the decision to look for and select a published mathematics test is accompanied by the desire to fulfill one of the following purposes: placement and grouping, diagnosis of pupil difficulties, assessment of progress of individual pupils, prediction of the probable success of pupils in certain courses, or evaluation of a new text, technique, unit, or curriculum. When tests are selected and used with a clear purpose in mind, the chances are much better that the whole undertaking will not be a waste of time. If a survey achievement test is being selected, it is necessary to know the particular course emphases and objectives before the selection is made. This is why the mathematics teacher is probably the only person in a school qualified to select a mathematics test for his course. For example, if a geometry achievement test is being selected, it is necessary to know the answers to the following questions: Are space ideas interwoven with the course? How much coordinate geometry was taught? What is the emphasis on the nature of proof and propositional logic? Is algebra involved to any extent? The answers have a great bearing on the appropriateness of a given achievement test in geometry.

The particular test chosen may be different for different schools, but the process of wise selection requires consideration of the same points, such as (a) the nature of the pupil population, (b) the content and objectives of the curriculum, (c) the purposes of testing, (d) the ways test scores may be used to accomplish these purposes, (e) the readiness, willingness, and ability of the school staff to administer tests and interpret scores, and (f) the amount of time and money available for testing. Each of these topics is fully discussed in a pamphlet by Martin R. Katz (1).

Selecting a Test

One of the first things a teacher should do in considering the use of a mathematics test is to take the test under the timed conditions. No casual reading is adequate for selection purposes. After taking the test, the teacher is in a position to judge its appropriateness in content and difficulty. Then he should consider such questions as the following: Are the questions in general fair for this class and this course? Are the questions mathematically sound? (Errors of this type are extremely rare but possible in a published mathematics test.) Are the questions mathematically interesting? Is the vocabulary and reading in the test suitable? Would the test be easy to administer and easy to take in terms of pupil directions and format? Is the test likely to be speeded or unspeeded for your class and does this agree with the way it was purportedly normed? Can the test be conveniently administered in a school period? How good are printing and layout? Some of these may be answered by giving the test to one or two typical students under timed conditions and then discussing with them some of the points listed above.

Examining a Typical Manual

When the teacher has taken the test and has answered the questions above, he should examine the manual and accessory materials. What should he look for now? Let us imagine that you are considering the use of an end-of-course achievement test in first-year algebra. Yours is an average class with few students at the high and low ability levels. You are examining a typical manual of a first-year algebra test. What will you find in it and what is important in your selection?

Content. On the first page of the manual there is an outline dividing the content into the two main categories under the headings "Meaning" and "Skill." There are six to nine subheadings under each of these. Then there is a statement that 25 percent of the items measure "Meaning" and 75 percent measure both "Meaning" and "Skill." Your first question should be: "Is this description in agreement with my judgment as a teacher?" It would be very appropriate at this point, since you have already taken the test, to draw up a tally sheet with the subheadings listed in the outline and to classify all the items in the test yourself. You may consider the claims of the manual reasonably valid by your standards if you come within 5 or 10 percent of the claimed figures.

Development of the Test. Under this topic in our typical manual the eight sources cited for objectives and content seem to indicate that the test was designed for the average student without regard to college plans. The pretest procedures in the initial tryout of the items seem to be adequate and careful. An intelligence test was given to the 2000 students in the pretest sample, so that the mean IQ is known for the pretest group. This helps in interpreting the difficulty values for each item, which are presented in an accompanying table. The validity indices of items mentioned at this point in the manual are really coefficients of discrimination between the high and low groups on the test. Pretest measures of difficulty and discrimination of items on a known population are necessary for all scientific test construction.

Reliability and Equivalence of Forms. The corrected split-half reliability coefficients are .85 and .88 for the two forms. These are good estimates of the true reliability and would be considered acceptable since this is a power, rather than a speeded test. Reliability in this manual is interpreted in terms of the standard error of measurement. This is given as 4.9 standard score points, which means that there are two chances in three that an individual's score on the test does not differ by more than 4.9 standard score points from his hypothetical *true* score. The discussion of equivalence of forms indicates that careful procedures were used to achieve balance among the forms with respect to content, item difficulty, and discrimination indices. The two forms may, therefore, be used to compare the performances of two different classes or the same class at two different points in time.

Directions for Scoring. Scoring directions seem to be clear and easy to follow. Time limits are given twice to the teacher and once in directions to the student, in addition to the statement on the front cover of the test. Separate directions for hand and machine scoring are provided.

Interpretation of Results. An adequate treatment seems to be given "Interpretation of Results" and "Using the Test Results," although ability in these areas develops more from experience than from reading. Scores are easily converted to end-of-year percentile ranks by means of a table that is provided. The manual states that the test was standardized on 3,183 cases in 57 schools representing 22 states throughout the country, and it rightly cautions against assuming this population to be a truly representative national sample. It goes on to suggest that the teacher using the test should note whether his group is below, at, or above the median IQ for the norms sample.

Other Materials

Other accessory materials available with the test consist of machine-scored answer sheets, perforated scoring stencil, expectancy chart, and class record chart.

Since most of the desirable technical features of a mathematics test seem to have been fulfilled by this test, the important determining question for you is, "Does this test sample behaviors at a level appropriate for my particular class?" If you have done the job of selection described above, then you, and only you, will be in a position to answer this question.

Summary

This chapter discusses procedures for the selection of published mathematics tests. Various methods of classifying tests are described. An inventory of 109 available published tests is given in a table with tests classified by purpose and subject. Some of the auxiliary materials published with tests, such as tally and record sheets and interpretive manuals, are described. The use of interpretive data to be found in manuals is developed. Some of the values of published mathematics tests are pointed out. The actual process of selecting a test and examining the contents of a good interpretive manual is outlined in detail. An annotated list of mathematics tests published since 1940 appears in the Appendix.

References

1. Katz, Martin R. *Selecting an Achievement Test*. Evaluation and Advisory Service Series No. 3. Princeton, N.J.: Educational Testing Service, 1958. 32 p.

2. Myers, Sheldon S. *Mathematics Tests Available in the United States*. Washington, D.C.: National Council of Teachers of Mathematics, April 1959. 12 p.

7

Appraising Attitudes in the Learning of Mathematics

MARY CORCORAN and E. GLENADINE GIBB

THE ATTITUDES of students toward mathematics play a vital part in their learning. We hope they will develop favorable attitudes as a result of our teaching, but these important aspects of learning are rarely considered in evaluating a student's achievement in mathematics. The reason is obvious; suitable instruments have not been widely available, and teachers are understandably hesitant about constructing their own devices in areas where there are few guideposts.

The purpose of this chapter is to encourage teachers to begin appraising these hard-to-test aspects of mathematics learning. We shall give primary emphasis to describing and illustrating a variety of ways in which attitudes may be appraised. The discussion is deliberately non-technical, and no attempt has been made to review the extensive literature available on attitudes and their measurement.

The basic principles of evaluation outlined by Hartung in Chapter 3 apply also to attitude appraisal. There are special problems, however, in obtaining unbiased evidence of attitudes, and it is more difficult to establish validity for measures of attitudes than for measures of achievement.

Nature of Attitudes

Definitions of attitudes vary in the features emphasized depending on the writer's viewpoint. Important for the study of attitudes toward mathematics is the idea that an attitude involves both cognitive and non-cognitive aspects—that is, both beliefs and feelings about the object of the attitudes. A student's attitude toward mathematics is, for example, a composite of intellectual appreciation of the subject and emotional reactions to it.

Direction and Intensity

In studying the attitudes of students toward mathematics (or any other subject), two important dimensions are direction *(Does the student generally like or dislike the subject?)* and intensity *(How strongly does the student feel about this attitude?)*. The student who feels that his attitude is well expressed by the statement: "Mathematics thrills me, and I like it better than any other subject," shows a stronger interest than one who says that his attitude is better described by the statement: "Sometimes I enjoy the challenge presented by a mathematics problem." Other aspects of individual attitudes that we sometimes study are consistency (the extent to which an attitude toward one aspect of the subject agrees with an attitude toward another), salience (the importance the individual attaches to the attitude), and public vs. private quality (the extent to which the individual is willing to reveal his feelings).

Most studies of students' attitudes toward mathematics have been concerned with the direction and intensity of attitudes regarding mathematics in general. While there is good reason to begin with a general measure of this sort, more specific attitudes may also merit study. These include attitudes toward specific mathematics courses and such specific aspects of mathematics as computation, problem solving, and figure construction. Attitudes about mathematics teachers, about the way mathematics is taught, and about the setting in which it is taught would form a second class of referents. Still other areas of exploration include the student's reaction to the difficulty of mathematics (the extent to which he regards it as a challenge or a hard subject), his interest (whether he is very curious about mathematics or finds it dull and boring), and the kind of value he uses to justify its study (whether he thinks mathematics should be studied because it is practical or thinks it is worth studying because it is intrinsically interesting).

Methods of Appraising Attitudes

While there is no direct way to observe a student's attitude about anything, inferences may be made about an underlying attitude by observing what a person says and does in relevant situations. Actually, attitudes are no different from a number of other human characteristics such as intelligence, taste, and judgment, for which we must also use indirect methods of appraisal. However, there may be more reason to conceal or distort the behavior through which attitudes are exhibited than there is for other types of behavior. Consequently, every attempt must be made to provide an atmosphere in which the student can feel confident in expressing himself freely.

The way an attitude study is introduced and the student's perception about how the information will be used are of particular importance for *self-report* procedures. There is a variety of methods for evaluating by self-report: the student reports his own attitudes by responding to a questionnaire or rating scale, or he describes his feelings by writing an essay or keeping a diary. There are other approaches, which we shall refer to as *observer-reports,* in which another person, perhaps the teacher, observes and records behavior that gives evidence of interests, attitudes, curiosity and related reactions. A third approach, the *interview,* involves both the student and an observer.

A distinction may also be made between procedures based on observation in a natural situation and those devised especially for the study of attitudes. Further distinctions may be made with respect to the degree of awareness on the part of the student that his attitudes are being appraised. When teachers make informal judgments about students' attitudes on the basis of observation in and out of the classroom, the situations are natural ones, and the students may not even realize that their attitudes are being appraised. The questionnaire, on the other hand, represents a specially structured situation, and the purpose is usually apparent. Structured situations in which the purpose may not be apparent involve the interview and those procedures using essays, diaries, special types of questionnaires (incomplete sentences, for example), and other projective techniques.

Because the self-report procedures have been much better developed than other attitude appraisal methods, and more examples of such instruments may be drawn on for illustrations, we give them a considerable amount of attention. We hope, however, that some teachers will be adventurous enough to use these ideas as starting points for other procedures in trying them out with their own students.

Self-Report Methods

For accurate reports, individuals should not be asked to make generalizations about their behavior, but should be given the opportunity to describe and to respond to questions about specific activities and events from relatively recent experiences. This should be done in an atmosphere that encourages the student to express his opinions freely.

Self-report instruments vary in the degree to which they give guidance to the individual making the report as well as in the extent to which he perceives their purpose. The most restricting is the questionnaire in which the student considers only those topics about which he is asked. The most flexible are the essays and diary records of mathematical activities where the student makes his own choice of content.

Questionnaires. Opinion questionnaires, rating forms, and check lists of various types have been devised to provide standard situations in which attitudes may be studied. Because all students are presented with the same verbal stimulus, and they indicate their responses in the same way, we may score objectively and compare responses of students. Such procedures permit a quantitative description of attitudes with consequent ease in handling the information.

A variety of such opinion and attitude rating forms has been developed ranging from those which are simply a list of opinion questions to those utilizing elaborately constructed scales that incorporate some of the more sophisticated work of specialists in psychological measurement. Some attempts have also been made to develop disguised attitude questionnaires. Since most teachers do not require fine differentiations of student attitudes, they can make good use of rather broad groupings of students into high, middle, and low ranking with respect to some attitudinal dimension. Instruments that might be relatively crude for a research purpose may, therefore, provide considerable information for the classroom teacher.

There are many situations in which a single question or a brief series of questions may provide useful information about attitudes on a particular point. For example, we may ask students to select from a list those topics they would like to pursue further and those topics they have no interest in studying further. The number of topics placed in each category provides one measure of general attitude toward the course. The assignment of specific topics is also of interest. Again, one may try to find out the extent of interest in mathematics and in various other school subjects by asking the student how much longer he would like to study them.

Groups of questions may also be used to appraise specific attitudes toward mathematics. For example, the items in Figure 1 may be used to identify those students with a high level of curiosity about mathematics and those with relatively little interest in the subject.

When responses to such items are analyzed separately, each item constitutes a scale in itself. While useful comparisons may often be made between such responses for one group of students and for another (for example, groups with different levels of ability, or groups of boys and girls), their reliability for the appraisal of an individual student's attitudes would be questionable. For this purpose attitude scales based on a number of items, each of which is designed to measure some aspect of the same attitude, are preferred.

Directions: Check each of the following by placing the appropriate answer in the space in front of the statement. Use the letters A, U, and D in giving your answers.

    A—Agree   U—Undecided   D—Disagree

_____1. I get more out of solving problems than out of practice exercises.

_____2. I like mathematics because you can figure things out instead of memorizing.

_____3. The harder the problems, the better I like to try them.

_____4. I like to try to solve mathematics problems that have "tricks" to them.

_____5. There is more to mathematics than just getting the right answer.

_____6. I never know what to do when I start an assignment.

Figure 1. Sample attitude questionnaire.

Attitude Scales. Several procedures have been developed for constructing attitude scales. Probably the most widely used is that developed by Likert. Each item in a *Likert-type scale* consists of a statement with which the student is asked to indicate agreement or disagreement. Very often this is done on a three-point scale ("agree," "uncertain," "disagree") or a five-point scale ("strongly agree," "agree," "uncertain," "disagree," and "strongly disagree").

The items in Figure 2, selected from the Hoyt-MacEachern Arithmetic Inventory (3), illustrate the type of statements used. The pupils are instructed, "Please read each statement carefully and decide whether it describes the way you feel about arithmetic." The pupils are instructed to mark response "A" if they agree with the statement, and "D" if they disagree. If they neither agree nor disagree, they are to mark the "U" response, but they are not encouraged to use this response for more than an occasional statement.

The statements for a Likert-type scale are collected in a variety of ways. The free responses of students in interviews or essays are a useful source for such statements. The preferred procedure is first to develop more items than will be needed for the final scale, and then to weed out those that do not contribute much to the total score.

The initial scoring is usually based on a judgmental scale for each item. The author attaches high and low scores to the responses on the basis of his judgment as to their position with respect to the attitude question. For example, the first item on the Hoyt-MacEachern scale, "I would like to take arithmetic even if it were not required" was scored 3 for "agree," 2 for "uncertain," and 1 for "disagree." The total score is the sum of scores on all items. Assuming that such a total score is a fairly good approximation of the students' attitudes, it can

	A	U	D
1. I would like to take arithmetic even if it were not required.			
4. I don't care whether I understand how to do a problem as long as I can get the right answer.			
21. I like to do a lot of problems of the same kind rather than have different kinds all mixed up.			
24. I would be interested in taking other subjects that make use of arithmetic.			
27. We shouldn't have questions on tests about things we haven't covered in class.			
69. I like to work problems in my head.			

Figure 2. Likert-type attitude scale, from Hoyt-MacEachern Arithmetic Inventory.

then be used as a basis for selecting items. The items to which high-scoring students give consistently different responses from low-scoring students are selected for the final scale. Although this is the usual procedure, other criteria are sometimes used for the selection of the most useful items. The Hoyt-MacEachern scale is an example of the practice described above. The criterion used in developing final scoring keys for this scale was the discrepancy between a student's score on an arithmetic achievement test and the achievement test score that would have been predicted on the basis of his aptitude test scores. It is interesting to note that while the use of an "outside" criterion did introduce some refinements in the scoring of this scale, a comparison of papers scored on both the judged weightings and the computed score weights has indicated that in most cases students are placed in the same relative position in their group by both scoring procedures.

Prior to the development of the Likert-type scale, the procedure developed by Thurstone was the best known. It is still used for appraising attitudes in a variety of circumstances. The purpose of the *Thurstone scaling method* is to obtain an attitude measure in which equal differences in scores have the same meaning in all parts of the scale. For instance, the difference between a score of 3 and a score of 7 is assumed to mean the same difference in intensity of attitude as that between 5 and 9. This is not necessarily true of Likert-type scales.

To construct a Thurstone-type scale one begins by collecting a large number of statements relative to the attitude under study. These statements are typed on separate slips of paper and distributed to a number of judges, preferably 50 or more, who are asked to sort the statements into groups based on the extent to which they view each statement as a favorable or unfavorable opinion with respect to the subject under study. Note that they are not asked to indicate their own opinions, but simply to grade the statements with respect to the degree to which a favorable or unfavorable opinion is expressed. Usually, the slips are sorted into 11 groups. The number of the group to which each judge assigns each statement is recorded as a score value. Then the scores assigned to each statement by the various judges are tabulated. Both the average score and the degree of consistency in the assigned scores are considered in selecting about 20 items for the final scale. Items on which the judges were generally in agreement in their classifications are selected at various points on the score scale, as indicated by their average scores. A scale developed by Dutton is an example of the Thurstone type. Figure 3 presents Dutton's attitude statements (2:19). The student checks those statements with which he agrees. The scale values, which are used for scoring the responses, do not appear on the actual scale. The average of the scale values of the statements checked is the student's attitude score.

In addition to the Thurstone and Likert techniques, many other attitude scale procedures have been developed. One of the most promising of these, the *Guttman-type scale,* is now more likely to be useful in research projects than in classroom studies. This scale is designed to measure a single attitude rather than a combination of several attitudes. The criterion for constructing these scales is a characteristic termed reproducibility; informally interpreted, this means that if we know a student's response to any one item, we can predict with a high degree of accuracy what he would say in response to all other items in the scale. Figure 4 is an example of a Guttman-type scale constructed to test attitudes of youth toward science (5).

The items are presented here in order of score level. If a student

Scale Value	Attitude Statement
9.5	_____ 1. I think about arithmetic problems outside of school and like to work them out.
3.7	_____ 2. I don't feel sure of myself in arithmetic.
8.6	_____ 3. I enjoy seeing how rapidly and accurately I can work arithmetic problems.
5.6	_____ 4. I like arithmetic, but I like other subjects just as well.
7.7	_____ 5. I like arithmetic because it is practical.
4.6	_____ 6. I don't think arithmetic is fun, but I always want to do well in it.
5.3	_____ 7. I am not enthusiastic about arithmetic, but I have no real dislike for it either.
5.9	_____ 8. Arithmetic is as important as any other subject.
3.3	_____ 9. Arithmetic is something you have to do even though it is not enjoyable.
7.0	_____10. Sometimes I enjoy the challenge presented by an arithmetic problem.
2.5	_____11. I have always been afraid of arithmetic.
9.0	_____12. I would like to spend more time in school working arithmetic.
1.0	_____13. I detest arithmetic and avoid using it at all times.
6.7	_____14. I enjoy doing problems when I know how to work them well.
3.2	_____15. I avoid arithmetic because I am not very good with figures.
10.5	_____16. Arithmetic thrills me, and I like it better than any other subject.
9.8	_____17. I never get tired of working with numbers.
2.0	_____18. I am afraid of doing word problems.
8.1	_____19. Arithmetic is very interesting.
1.5	_____20. I have never liked arithmetic.
10.4	_____21. I think arithmetic is the most enjoyable subject I have taken.
3.0	_____22. I can't see much value in arithmetic.

Figure 3. Thurstone-type attitude scale, from a study by Wilbur H. Dutton (2), copyright 1956 by the University of Chicago.

responds "no" to item 1, there is a high probability that he will say "no" to all those further down on the list. If, however, he says "yes" to items 1 and 2 and "no" to item 3, he will probably say "no" to the remaining items, even though they would not be presented to him in this order, but in a random sequence. In other words, at whatever point in the above list he responds "no," he will most likely respond "no" to the remaining items. This scale may be scored either on the basis of the number of "yes" answers or by a weighted system.

Do you think scientists can provide solutions to the following problems?

	Yes	Probably Yes	Probably No	No
1. New defense weapons	___	___	___	___
2. Cures for diseases	___	___	___	___
3. New farming products	___	___	___	___
4. How to cure mental illness	___	___	___	___
5. How to best educate students to be good citizens	___	___	___	___
6. Juvenile delinquency	___	___	___	___

Figure 4. Guttman-type attitude scale, from Purdue Opinion Panel report.

Incomplete Sentences. The incomplete sentence technique has certain of the practical administrative advantages of the questionnaire or attitude scale, but gives the student much more freedom to respond in his own way. Incomplete sentences may be described as "open-end" statements designed to stimulate responses in specific areas of attitude while allowing the individual considerable freedom in his choice of response. However, the reply may be partly controlled by the content and grammatical structure of the sentence beginning (1). To appraise a student's feelings about mathematics, stems should elicit responses that will reveal his reactions to the subject. As with any means of self-reporting, students vary in their willingness to express themselves. A time limit and instructions not to spend a long time in completing any one sentence will tend to encourage spontaneous responses.

Illustrative stems, with examples of the kinds of responses which students make, are shown in Figure 5. Responses to many sentence stems may be evaluated simply in terms of the general direction of the attitude expressed or by such categories of responses as reactions to the difficulty of the subject, reactions to teaching, beliefs about why the subject should be studied, or other aspects of interest to the evaluator.

The incomplete sentence method falls into the general category of projective techniques—those procedures in which the individual has an opportunity to organize and interpret material in a way that expresses his own feelings. Another approach that is now being used in research studies of attitudes about mathematics involves the use of pictures. A student is shown a picture and is asked to write a paragraph telling what he thinks is happening and what led up to the situation. The pictures might, for example, show a teacher and a mathematics class, an engineer working a problem, or a research scientist in his laboratory.

Directions: Using the following as the beginning of your sentence, write a complete sentence. You may complete it in any way you wish. There is no one sentence that should be written.

Stems	*Sample Responses*
I should like to know	more about numbers and systems of numeration.
	if I can use what I have learned.
	more about percents and formulas.
This course has kept me	very busy as mathematics is very difficult.
	alert.
	fairly busy.
	busy and confused.
When we have our mathematics class, I	sometimes like it and sometimes not.
	work.
	usually don't have my lesson.
	pay very close attention.
	don't know what to expect.
	always learn something new.

Figure 5. Examples of incomplete sentence technique.

Results with this approach depend on the effectiveness of the pictures in stimulating significant responses. No scoring categories have yet been developed. Experiences with a similar technique used for other purposes, however, suggest that the picture-story approach may reveal a student's predominant motives for the study of mathematics—for example, to achieve, to satisfy others, or to gain power over others—as well as his general attitude toward the subject.

Essays. A simple projective procedure, easily adapted to classroom use, is the familiar essay. Topics may be chosen that will elicit reactions to specific aspects of mathematics learning or they may be quite general, intended to allow each student to choose the particular topics of most concern to himself. For example, brief essays that were written by eighth grade students in a mathematics class on the general subject "What I Think About Mathematics," contained frequent comments about a new type of subject matter which they were being taught. These comments were of two quite different types. Some students found considerable challenge and interest in the new material, as expressed in these excerpts from two essays:

> I like math more than any other subjects. I used to think I didn't, but that was when I was in grade school and I associated it with only arithmetic (which is not always so very interesting). I find mathematics different and fun. There's sort of a challenge in it. . . . You have to have an "open mind" to understand math and accept it. Sometimes this is hard, but I like it.

*   *   *

> I enjoy mathematics on the whole quite a bit. Right now I don't especially like the adding and subtraction of small numbers. I like to work in modular arithmetic and I like talking about new systems. I think that too much of the Pythagorean Theorem can get boring, but a medium amount can be very interesting.

But others questioned the value of studying number systems because they didn't believe these had any practical use:

> Personally I feel math is a challenge. It gives me a chance to try to figure out things. I enjoy working with numbers, but there are certain things that I've had here that I feel are not important for everyday use—Base 7, prime numbers, etc. These may be done for fun or extra, but are not the base for a class hour.

*   *   *

> When I started school we had simple math that I thought was necessary. But as I enter the eighth grade I was pretty sure that this (eighth grade arithmetic) was not necessary. I think others in this room would think different but it would not help me in my future. . . . I will admit that the equation bit is much better than the number line junk. But I think it would be much better to stick to straight math all through the school years.

These essays also included reactions to the way the course was taught, to the homework assignments, and to the grades received.

The essay is adaptable to use at varying grade levels as the following illustrative topic questions indicate:

What do you think about mathematics? What do you like best about it? What do you like least about it?

What would you like to learn next year in mathematics? Why?

Should all high school students be required to study mathematics? What is your opinion and why do you think so?

What do you think the poet meant who said: "Euclid alone has looked on beauty bare"? Have you ever felt that way about any subject you studied?

There is a general belief that students will more freely express their opinions if the essays are left unsigned. Unsigned essays will provide the teacher with information for the class as a whole but not for individual students. It is likely that the general rapport between teacher and students has as much bearing on the candor of the essays as the question of whether or not they are signed.

Observational Methods

The projective techniques, including the essay, require subjective judgment on the part of the person interpreting the attitudes expressed. Observational procedures also require that judgment be made in deciding what to observe.

Classroom teachers make many such observations without any special intention to do so. They notice the extras that a student does, his unsolicited comments about his work, the tasks he seems to stick with longer than others. All these behaviors may give evidence of attitudes toward the subject. Such observations have the advantage of being based on natural situations that often represent experience with a student over an extended time period. However, they do suffer from the fact that people notice and remember only part of what they see, and the observer's own attitudes influence what he observes. To correct for bias in observations, certain procedures have been suggested, for example, making notes about specific incidents as they occur and describing such incidents precisely before attempting interpretation; observing students at scheduled times, using a check list as a guide for noting particular activities. One such check list, developed by the Mathematics Section of the Minnesota National Laboratory (4) as part of a teacher's log book, includes a section for recording evidences of interest, maturation, and curiosity as reflected in pupil activities (Fig. 6). This form is designed for recording observations of an entire class during one period. Similar items may be used for individual students.

Check List of Pupil Activities

Enter in the blanks at the left a single check ($\sqrt{}$) for each activity you observed at least *once for one or more pupils,* a double check ($\sqrt{}\sqrt{}$) for activities observed at least *once for a majority* of your pupils, and a triple check ($\sqrt{}\sqrt{}\sqrt{}$) for activities occurring *more than once for a majority* of the pupils.

Evidences of interest, motivation, curiosity

——1. Evidenced having studied assigned material.

——2. Evidenced having read or studied unassigned material.

——3. Evidenced having discussed work outside class with one another.

——4. Asked question(s) which indicated curiosity.

——5. Asked question(s) which indicated learning difficulty.

——6. Took notes on lecture, solution of problems at blackboard, etc.

——7. Aggressively kept trying to understand, solve problems, etc.

——8. Became frustrated; gave up trying to understand, solve problems, etc.

Figure 6. Check list for rating a class, prepared by the Mathematics Section of the Minnesota National Laboratory.

The intensity of observed student attitudes may be rated if the instrument provides an opportunity for indicating the degree of feeling expressed. Unless a student is demonstrative in his feelings, it will be more difficult for an observer to draw inferences about intensity of likes and dislikes than to note behaviors suggestive of interest, curiosity, and other motives for learning. The following scale designed for rating individual students suggests the kinds of behaviors that may be rated in this way.

Use the following code to indicate your observations: Always 5, Usually 4, Sometimes 3, Seldom 2, Never 1.

——1. Completes optional assignments.

——2. Works independently.

——3. Brings applications of mathematics to class.

——4. Reads in other books to get information about a topic studied in class.

——5. Asks questions about ideas he doesn't understand.

——6. Does independent projects.

——7. Is curious about many new ideas.

Figure 7. Sample check list for rating individual students.

Interviews

While teachers must generally rely heavily on attitude appraisal procedures that may be used for the class group as a whole, individual study procedures will at times be advisable. If, for example, inconsistencies are found between the student's own statement of attitudes and those inferred by the teacher, or if the student's level of achievement is not what might be expected on the basis of aptitude test data, further study on an individual basis would be recommended. In such instances valuable information may be obtained from skillfully handled interviews designed to provide the student with an opportunity for free expression of his feelings about the class, the subject, and perhaps other matters that seem to be of concern to him. Interviews need not, however, be restricted to use with students who present special problems. Indeed teachers may profitably plan to have such interviews with students periodically, whether or not a special problem exists.

Most teacher interviewers will need to do some preplanning for the questions they will use, but the teacher should feel free to follow up any line of discussion or pick up additional relevant topics introduced by students. In reporting the behavior observed in an interview, attention should be given to the facial expression, tone of voice, enthusiasm, and readiness with which the student replies, as well as to the words themselves. It may be easier to concentrate on such non-verbal expression if a tape recording is made of the interview responses. Much may be lost if the interviewer tries to record all seemingly pertinent information by taking notes or marking a check list. Furthermore, information that may not seem pertinent at the time of an interview may become significant as the interview progresses or after it has been completed.

Interpretation of Attitude Data

The attitude appraisal methods described in the previous section yield data of various types. The quantitative measures provided by attitude scales may be used to rank individuals with respect to the attitude variable. Attitude measures of this type may be interpreted for classes of students and, with caution, for individual students in much the same manner as classroom achievement test scores (see Chapter 4).

Responses to single attitude items in which pre-assigned categories such as "agree" and "disagree" are checked lend themselves to straightforward handling. A tabulation may be made of the number of students giving each response to an item, and the percentage may be determined. If the group is large enough to warrant subdivision, it may be valuable to tabulate by such subgroups as boys and girls; high, middle, and low ability groups; or age groups. Cross-tabulation of responses to different items or comparisons of the teacher's rating with the student's rating of himself on a particular matter can provide data for identifying important relationships between attitudes and other variables.

Significant insights reflecting students' thinking and feeling about mathematics may be obtained from procedures that do not lend themselves to the counting of responses or to numerical comparisons. Data collected in the form of anecdotal records, interviews, recordings, essays, and other free-response materials are of this type. Procedures for the analysis of these data depend on the aspect that is of interest and the purpose for which data will be used. If the teacher is primarily interested in enlarging his own understanding of the way students think about various aspects of mathematics, it may be sufficient if he carefully reads the materials collected and makes notes of points that seem especially important because of the intensity or the frequency of their mention.

This preliminary reading is needed, in a more systematic analysis, as a basis for deciding how to categorize responses. It is then helpful to outline a tentative classification scheme, distinguishing between *what is said* and *how it is said*. Subheadings under *what is said* would be related to the subject matter—what the student mentions, the direction of attitude he indicates, and the kinds of reasons he gives for his opinions. Under *how it is said* one would be particularly interested in noting evidences of intensity or strength of attitude as seen in the way the student expresses himself. When a large amount of material must be analyzed, it is advisable to set up codes for the various categories, allowing for later extensions as they are needed. The papers or other records may then be reviewed independently by two coders and their classifications of the data may be compared. After data have been coded, tabulations of the frequency of various categories may be readily made and the resulting data analyzed in a manner similar to that suggested above for structured response data.

Validity of Attitude Data

While the primary aim of this chapter is to encourage teachers to make appraisals of attitudes, and while a variety of methods for making such appraisals has been suggested, it would be unwise to conclude without advising caution in the interpretation of attitude data. It must be recognized that in none of these procedures has the problem of validity been solved. The usual method for appraising the validity of an attitude measurement instrument involves a logical judgment that the information obtained is relevant to the attitude presumed to be measured. Some attempts have been made to validate attitude measures in terms of the extent to which verbal responses are related to outside criterion measures of the attitude. For mathematics, such a criterion might be the student's subsequent choice of mathematics courses as electives. However, the criterion in such cases may present as much of a validity problem as the original instrument. Another approach is to hypothesize, on the basis of theoretical considerations, relationships that would be expected to exist between the attitude measured and other behavior that can be observed, and then to test whether or not these predictions are borne out by the evidence. It has been hypothesized, for example, that an attitude measure would predict the discrepancies between actual achievement scores and scores that would be predicted on the basis of the student's ability level. Although findings in some studies have supported this hypothesis, the matter is still open to speculation.

Reliability of Attitude Data

Another point that should be considered in interpreting attitude measurements is their reliability. The reliability of attitude appraisals, just as that of other types of measurement, is affected by the number of samples on which such appraisals are based. It is important, therefore, to recognize that the single question or observation may provide quite unstable information. If a teacher presents a question at different times to the same group of students and compares the answers, he will obtain a clue as to the stability with which the group tends to respond to questions of this type. Similarly, observations of students may be repeated and the ratings compared.

Attitude material of a qualitative nature presents the additional problem of rater-reliability. Care in plans for coding such material and some review of coding discrepancies will lead to considerable improvement in rater agreement. Evidence of the extent to which lack of reliability must be considered in the use of data on attitudes may be obtained by checking a teacher's evaluations from time to time with those of another person.

When test-retest reliabilities are computed, it is noted that the measurement of attitudes seems to be less reliable than that of the achievement areas. This may be due to actual fluctuations in the attitudes or to the limited sampling of behavior on which most attitude measures are based. Measures of internal consistency reliability, such as the Kuder-Richardson procedures described in Chapter 4, often yield reliabilities in the .70's and even the .80's with well-constructed attitude scales in which a well-defined attitude object is appraised. Reliability measurements of this type tend to be measurements of the generality or specificity of the attitude under study as well as of the consistency in responses to a set of items supposedly sampling the same area.

Use of Attitude Data

If students' attitudes toward mathematics learning are important, both as indicators of what they have learned and as elements in motivation for further learning, attitude appraisal should not be left out of the evaluation program. It is true that the available instruments have many deficiencies and that much research and imaginative exploration of new approaches to attitude appraisal are needed if better procedures are to be developed. But what can the conscientious teacher do right now?

Sometimes teachers have been led to believe that there is no point in evaluating something unless the evaluation can be performed well. In practice many judgments must be made on the basis of less than complete data. A more defensible position would call for care in the interpretation of any single piece of attitude evidence, since it may, indeed, provide an incomplete picture of the student's true position. But different judgments may be checked against one another with the accumulation of items of evidence from various sources. Such accumulated information from a number of sources over a period of time may be expected to provide a useful basis for appraising the attitudes of a group of students toward mathematics and the feeling of any individual Jack or Jane.

References

1. DOLE, ARTHUR A., and FLETCHER, FRANK M. "Some Principles in the Construction of Incomplete Sentences." *Educational and Psychological Measurement* 15: 101-10; Summer 1955.

2. DUTTON, WILBUR H. "Attitudes of Junior High School Pupils Toward Arithmetic." *School Review* 64: 18-22; January 1956.

3. HOYT, CYRIL J., and MACEACHERN, DONALD G. *An Investigation of the Interrelationship Among Attitudes Toward Arithmetic, Various Aspects of Achievement in Arithmetic, and Mental Ability of Junior High School Pupils*. Minneapolis: University of Minnesota, Bureau of Educational Research, June 1958. (An unpublished study.)

4. MINNESOTA NATIONAL LABORATORY, MATHEMATICS SECTION. *Log Book*.

Minneapolis: University of Minnesota, Bureau of Educational Research, December 1960.

5. PURDUE OPINION PANEL. *Science Education and Civil Liberties.* Purdue Opinion Panel Report No. 51. Lafayette, Indiana: Purdue University, March 1958.

Evaluation Practices of
Selected Schools

ROBERT KALIN

THE AUTHORS of preceding chapters have focused our attention on many principles in the theory of evaluation that are important for mathematics education. The reader may naturally ask how the schools are using these theories in actual practice. This chapter will present, as a partial answer, statements by spokesmen for 18 selected schools or school systems describing specific procedures used in their evaluation programs. In this way theoretical principles stated in earlier chapters are illustrated by actual models.

The author was faced with the problem of finding and selecting schools using suitably illustrative evaluation techniques. To secure breadth and impartiality he initiated a national search, and he relied on informed opinion. Following is a brief summary of that search.

First, 48 state departments of education and 4 national authorities were asked to name schools or school systems with outstanding evaluation programs in mathematics. The intent was to obtain recommendations from well-informed and responsible people who could wisely select good programs. The result was the recommendation of 119 schools in 30 states.

The second step was to request representatives in 115 of these schools to supply outlines of their testing programs. Of these, 67 responded. The responses revealed that these schools were using a variety of procedures in many ways at several grade levels. Tests were both teacher-made and commercially produced. They included achievement, aptitude, diagnostic, and other test types. Results have been used for individual and for group guidance, for grades and for prediction, for selection and for advice, for curriculum planning and for instructional improvement. Some test construction techniques and various administrative procedures were noted.

But not all 67 schools employed practices compatible with theoretical recommendations in this yearbook, and there were numerous duplications. It was necessary, therefore, to select those schools or school systems practicing specific evaluation techniques that best exemplify theories prescribed elsewhere in the yearbook; 35 were so selected. A representative of each was asked to supply a short description of specially-chosen features of his school's evaluation program. Such descriptions were received from 21 of the selected 35.

The discovery and selection process was then complete, making it possible to illustrate how some schools are using specific procedures recommended in the theory of evaluation for mathematics education. Following are 18 illustrative statements, each written by a representative from a selected school. To provide credits and to maintain continuity, the author has inserted some introductory, contextual remarks.

Descriptions of Selected Evaluation Practices

Selection of Students for Accelerated Programs

Many schools are much concerned now with the development of programs for the mathematically talented; these are the so-called accelerated, advanced placement, or honors programs. Selection of students is a problem whose solution may be aided by intelligent use of evaluation techniques. For example, Margaret L. Thomas, Director of Guidance and Testing for the Fresno City Unified School District of California, reports that in the Fresno Schools:

At the junior high school level an attempt is made to identify students with unusual mathematical potential, and to counsel them into the beginning course of an accelerated mathematics program and into subsequent courses for the remainder of their secondary school career. Basically, this advanced offering is initiated in grade 8 with beginning algebra, a course which is normally given to average students in grade 9. The acceleration program continues with geometry in grade 9 and a second year of algebra in grade 10. Grade 11 offerings are one semester each of trigonometry and of mathematics survey. (The latter is an introduction to college mathematics.) Analytics and calculus are scheduled for twelfth grade students, providing an opportunity to enter college with a strong preparation for advanced work there.

Screening for this accelerated program is done in the spring semester of grade 7. Selection of students is based on several factors. The California

Arithmetic Test, Junior High Level, is administered; students scoring a mathematics grade placement of two years above actual school placement are considered. Teachers and counselors then study the school records of this group of boys and girls to check on previous grades, social and emotional maturity, general physical health, work habits, industriousness and general scholastic aptitude.

Judgments are not made on the basis of test results alone. The ever-present possibility of errors in group testing is recognized, and flexibility in decisions comes through evaluating each student on the basis of past achievement, demonstrated interest in mathematics, and above-average ability.

Contact is made with parents of the selected boys and girls to explain the proposed program. In each case parental approval is secured before the student is scheduled into the advanced course.

The Savannah-Chatham County Public School System of Georgia uses similar selection techniques, even though it is located in a different geographical region and its secondary school curriculum differs slightly from that in Fresno, California. Note that Associate Superintendent of Curriculum and Research, H. Titus Singletary, Jr., and Director of Pupil Study and Appraisal, Ruth M. Folger, also mention the necessity of follow-up of the selection process:

Minimum requirements for students participating in this gifted-child program are:

1. Student should be able to succeed easily in seventh grade arithmetic, maintaining at least a "B" average.
2. Student should score approximately two years beyond grade level on a standardized arithmetic test.
3. The student's mental maturity must be above average.
4. The student must have good physical stamina and should be emotionally stable, in so far as these factors can be observed by the teacher.

Effort is made to select for these classes only those students whose identifying information would indicate a very high degree of success. Prediction seldom has a probability of one; hence, it is necessary to make a constant surveillance of the students' progress.

In the school year 1958-59, 94 seventh grade students with a median IQ of 125 and a median grade placement of 10.7 on a standardized arithmetic test were screened for three classes of first year algebra to be taken in the eighth grade.

All 94 students completed first-year algebra. The grades were distributed as follows: 84 students had above-average grades, 8 students had average grades, and 2 students had unsatisfactory grades. Those students with average and above-average grades enrolled in second-year algebra in the ninth grade.

Follow-up of initial student selection may be formalized into evaluation procedures designed to foster the program's success. The faculty at Nautilus Junior High School of Miami Beach, Florida, has devised one way of seeing that the selection has been fair and suitable to the student, the program, and the school. Note that the principal, Stuart D. Wooley, mentions the all-important factors of information to parents and parental decision:

To find students eligible for a seventh grade accelerated mathematics class, in the spring we recorded the most recent achievement and intelligence test scores of all sixth grade students likely to enter Nautilus Junior High in the fall. (There were 460 such students in 1959.) In addition, each sixth grade teacher was asked by our seventh grade counselor to tape-record comments about each student.

This composite information was used to rank these students. Eliminating health problems wherever possible and utilizing the teacher comments, we re-evaluated the ranking to finally select the top 105 students. They were placed in three home rooms of 35 students each upon entrance into our junior high school.

These three groups attended regular mathematics classes under three different mathematics teachers for the first six-week grading period. All three used similar lesson plans. During this time the entire seventh grade was tested (county-wide arithmetic testing program). This was a key point in our consideration, since it gave us up-to-date data on areas of strengths and weaknesses.

Now a meeting of the three mathematics teachers, the seventh grade counselor, and the principal was held. Utilizing teacher evaluation of the six weeks work, plus the new test data, a final list of 35 eligible students was made. The remaining 70 students were scheduled to either of the other two mathematics teachers in this experiment. Both of these classes received an enriched mathematics program befitting their capabilities. These three classes began to function in this manner at the start of the second grading period.

During this time, two communications had been sent home to the parents of these three groups. The first letter, early in September, explained the purpose of the forthcoming accelerated program and the activity their child might expect if assigned, and stated that no child would be assigned without his parents' approval. Parents were asked to indicate on this letter whether they would grant permission if their child were recommended, and to return the letter to school. A second letter was sent at the beginning of the seventh week notifying the parents of the 35 children who *were* assigned. In no case was any child placed in this class without the written approval of his parents.

Guidance for Ninth Grade Mathematics

Some kind of testing procedure is also necessary to guide students toward a proper choice when they face that important decision upon promotion to the ninth grade: algebra or general mathematics. Criteria for recommending students for ninth-grade mathematics courses have been developed at Warren City, Ohio. Table 1 contains a portion of the 5-point criteria table used at Warren City, as submitted by Assistant Superintendent for Curriculum and Instruction Wiley S. Garrett. You may note with interest that these categories are analogous to those used in Savannah, Georgia, for selection of the talented student.

TABLE 1

CRITERIA FOR GUIDANCE INTO ALGEBRA, WARREN CITY, OHIO

Guidance Data	Source
(1) 120 IQ or above	California Test of Mental Maturity
(2) 9.0 grade level or above	Stanford Achievement Test
(3) 3.5 average grade or above	Average of marks for academic subjects in 8th grade
(4) Teacher Estimate	Recommendation of algebra by 8th grade mathematics teacher based on estimation of ability, attitude, motivation, and application.
(5) Counselor Estimate	Recommendation of algebra by counselor based on chances for success from expectancy tables, meeting criteria of potential, achievement and marks, and the need for algebra for college entrance or for occupational choice.

(Editor's Note: The remainder of the Warren City table gives criteria for entrance into "Applied Mathematics or Algebra" or into "Arithmetic.")

One of the tests used to assist this guidance process at Warren City is the Lee Test of Algebraic Ability. Mr. Garrett reports that a five-part guidance report form is used in connection with this test to secure effective coordination among school, child, and parent. Table 2 shows a portion of this form.

As mentioned in Table 1, the Warren City schools use expectancy tables to assist in the algebra versus general mathematics decision process. This has been found an effective technique in Sioux Falls, South Dakota, as well. Director of Guidance Services Robert W. O'Hare

TABLE 2

GUIDANCE REPORT FORM, WARREN CITY, OHIO

Score of Lee Test_____ Percentile Rank_____
Mark in Arithmetic: 7th Grade_____ 8th Grade_____
Rating on Application:_____
                     (Very Good)   (Good)   (Fair)   (Questionable)
                     _____
                       (Poor)

(I)

Interpretation of Lee Test Score:

Lee Test Score	Percentile Rank	Chances for Success in Algebra
100 and above	75 – 99	Very Good
81 – 99	50 – 74	Good
60 – 80	24 – 49	Fair
50 – 59	13 – 23	Questionable
0 – 49	1 – 12	Poor

(II)

The student will check the statement that applies to him:
( ) I intend to go to college and algebra is required.
( ) I intend to take the Vocational Course, and algebra is required or desirable.
( ) The career I am interested in requires higher mathematics.
( ) The career I am interested in does not require higher mathematics.

(III)

Considering all the evidence, it is recommended that the student be enrolled in:
        Algebra_____Applied Mathematics_____Arithmetic_____
                        Counselor's Signature_____

(IV)

To Parents: (Check one)
    ( ) I have read the above and agree with the recommendation.
    ( ) I would like to have a conference with the arithmetic teacher and/or
        counselor.
                              Parent's Signature_____

(V)

Enrollment is approved for: Algebra_____Applied Mathematics_____
                             Arithmetic_____
                              Principal's Signature_____

describes the use of expectancy tables by posing a problem via the Mathematics Aptitude Chart in Table 3, another one of the counseling tools available to the Sioux Falls counselor.

TABLE 3

MATHEMATICS APTITUDE CHART, SIOUX FALLS, SOUTH DAKOTA

Name of Pupil (Last Name First)	Sioux Falls Percentiles				Arithmetic Grade 1st Semester 8th Grade	Use A (Algebra) or GM (General Math)		
	Differential Aptitude Tests			Iowa Test Arithmetic Total		Math Teacher's Recommendation	Student's Choice	Counselor's Recommendation
	Verbal (VA)	Numerical (NA)	VA + NA					
Student A	90	98	96	99	A	A	A	A
Student B	20	14	16	19	F	GM	GM	GM
Student C	50	65	60	35	D	GM	A	?
Student D	58	68	62	69	B−	A	GM	?

After citing the probable reasonableness of choices by students A and B, Mr. O'Hare says:

However, in the case of both Student C and Student D, the choice of the student is not fully in accord with the known data. In one case, the student has possibly overestimated his ability; in the other case, he has possibly underestimated his ability. Both cases call for careful counseling. Perhaps as a result of the conference with the student it will be necessary to ask the parents to come for an interview. In each junior high school the principal makes the final decision.

Specific cut-off points are not used. Likewise, no system of weights has been devised for the various criteria. But the counselor has the use of Expectancy Tables based on the results of the Differential Aptitude Test. These tables, used only when necessary, were devised by administering the Numerical Ability section of the DAT to second semester eighth graders. The following year, the end-of-the-year algebra grades were matched against the results of the Numerical Ability Test. Table 4 is based on 478 cases. The numbers have been rounded to ten to make for easy usage. (Although the total for each category comes to ten, an equal number of students did not score in each category.) For example, if a girl scored at the 96th percentile (Sioux Falls norms) or higher, one could say that based on the results of what other Sioux Falls students have experienced, her chances of receiving an "A" in algebra, provided she worked up to her ability, would be six out of ten.

TABLE 4

EXPECTANCY TABLE FOR GUIDANCE INTO ALGEBRA, SIOUX FALLS, SOUTH DAKOTA, GIRLS ONLY

Numerical Ability DAT Sioux Falls Percentile	Mark Received in Algebra End of Year, 9th Grade					
	F	D	C	B	A	TOTAL
95 +				4	6	10
79 – 94			3	5	2	10
53 – 78		1	5	3	1	10
33 – 52		4	5	1		10
15 – 32	1	6	3			10
1 – 14	9	1				10

Test Selection

But how do school systems decide what kind of test and which test should be used in a particular situation? Several techniques for doing this have been given in Chapter 6 of this yearbook. Director of Instructional Evaluation Joan K. Bollenbacher of the Cincinnati, Ohio, Public Schools describes how such a problem was faced and solved in her school system:

Advanced Placement Mathematics classes were offered in the Cincinnati public schools for the first time in September 1954. After three years' experience with the program it was decided that pupils should be sectioned at the beginning of the tenth grade for two years of advanced work in preparation for the actual Advanced Placement class in the senior year. It became necessary then to select students for the advanced classes during the second semester of the ninth grade.

After conferences with teachers, counselors, supervisors, and principals, it was decided that students would qualify on the basis of several criteria, one of which was a score of percentile rank 90 or above on a standardized achievement test in mathematics. In selecting the appropriate test, two alternatives seemed to be open. One was to use a mathematics test that measured achievement in fundamentals, including skills and understanding. Some persons expressed the opinion that the algebra test would be "more demanding" and consequently more appropriate. Others indicated that the recommendation of the algebra teacher (one of the five criteria) would yield in effect the same type of information as the algebra test but that a test of basic arithmetic processes would insure well-rounded preparation.

Some data had been gathered previously favoring the position of the latter group. In a study completed in 1957 in the Cincinnati public schools it was found that a standardized arithmetic achievement test given at the end of grade 8 proved to be the best single predictor of the three-year grade point average in mathematics. It was decided, however, that specific data regarding the effectiveness of the algebra test and the fundamentals test in predicting the success of capable students in algebra should be gathered. Accordingly, a standardized algebra test and the Cooperative Mathematics Test for Grades 7, 8, and 9 were administered to 100 capable students completing their study of first-year algebra. Appropriate correlations were computed comparing algebra marks and test scores. The correlation for the Cooperative Mathematics Test was slightly higher, although not significantly so. Since the Cooperative Test added another dimension to the selection process, it seemed appropriate to choose it.

It should be pointed out that although this selection procedure was based on the best available data in 1958, it will not be considered valid until a follow-up study can be completed. Since it is planned to use scores on the Advanced Placement Examinations as the validity criterion, this study cannot be completed until 1961 when the group will take the examinations.

Test Construction

Recently, teachers in the Washington, D. C., high schools also faced a test selection problem. But they arrived at a different type of solution —they constructed their own test. The reader will also note that the testing purpose was quite different: These District of Columbia teachers wanted to find a way to maintain uniform achievement standards in mathematics. Both Cincinnati and Washington used a variety of teacher participation in seeking a solution. (Some criticize conferences and committee work as inefficient. Regardless of the merit of this criticism, such participation can afford an opportunity for learning.)

Miss Carol McCamman, mathematics teacher at Calvin Coolidge High School, has provided this description of the Washington, D. C., experience:

The District of Columbia city-wide algebra test had its beginning in a 1956 panel discussion of standards and grading in mathematics, followed by a questionnaire to all mathematics teachers. While teachers disagreed as to whether a final mark should reflect such factors as interest, work habits, and citizenship (senior high teachers were *against* it 3 to 1, while junior high teachers were *in favor* 3 to 2), they were overwhelmingly in favor of uniformity of standards and marks in elementary algebra and the sequential mathematics in senior high.

A committee consisting of an algebra teacher from each of 18 schools met with the two mathematics supervisors and decided to have a city-wide algebra test, on an experimental basis, in the spring of 1957. Existing standardized tests were considered, but rejected, chiefly because they did not exactly fit the Washington course of study, or did not have enough forms to use year after year. The committee decided to construct its own test. Each committee member wrote ten multiple-choice questions on a section of the course of study. A small committee selected and edited 60 of these questions. The whole committee took the proposed test, following which there was further revision.

After school on the day the test was given, the algebra teachers met to correct the answer sheets using punched-out keys. A small committee tabulated scores and computed percentiles, so that the results could be returned to the schools the following day.

Since it was considered important to compare the teacher's rating of a pupil with his performance on the test, each algebra teacher was asked to submit, before the test, the estimated grades of the students. Comparison of these estimated grades with the test scores showed some extreme differences in grading. Students who rated A and B in some classes had poorer test scores than D and F students in some other classes. Class medians varied from 14 to 38 (of a possible 60). While such variation was to be expected since most of the junior highs use homogeneous grouping, it was found that in most cases teachers gave the full range of letter grades regardless of the ability of the group. Thus, although in replying to the questionnaire teachers said algebra students should *not* be graded in relation to the rest of the class, in practice most often they *were* being so graded.

Teachers in general were pleased with the test. They found it helpful in grading their students and in motivating them. The scores were an objective measure which pupils, parents, and principals could understand. Supervisors observed that the following year principals were selecting pupils for algebra more carefully, and teachers were adhering more closely to the course of study. The results of the second year's test showed much better correspondence between the teacher's estimated grade and the test score.

A city-wide algebra test has been constructed and administered in similar fashion each year since the first one. A geometry test is now being developed, and other departments are working on tests as part of a new program of final examinations in the high schools.

In the Tulsa, Oklahoma, public schools a number of tests have been developed for a variety of reasons. They have their own "Primary Arithmetic Test," administered at the end of Grade 3 or beginning of

Grade 4 for diagnostic and/or achievement purposes. Coy C. Pruitt, Supervisor of Mathematics, reports also that they have constructed tests and exercises for junior high mathematics and for the traditional senior high academic subjects. One test Mr. Pruitt views as having particular merit is an arithmetic test given in the eleventh year:

> This test was developed by teachers in two of our senior high schools and has been given to several thousand eleventh grade pupils. The original intent for this test was to determine whether or not an arithmetic refresher course should be recommended for certain seniors who were terminating their school work. We finally decided to recommend that all eleventh grade students falling below the first quartile take a refresher course in arithmetic in their twelfth year.

Item Construction

Good test construction requires good item construction. Carol Mc-Camman of Washington, D. C., hinted at this process in her discussion, and Max Sobel fully explores the topic in Chapter 5. Here Frank S. Hawthorne, Supervisor of Mathematics Education in New York State, describes the item construction procedure used in developing statewide achievement tests (the so-called Regents Examinations):

> Approximately a million New York State Regents Examinations are written every year. These examinations are constructed by committees of teachers working with representatives of the State Education Department. The mechanics of composing such examinations differ in the several subject fields, but the procedure in mathematics may be considered typical.
>
> Before the committee of five high school teachers and one college professor meets, the members each prepare a number of questions in rough draft form and exchange them, and later comment about them, by certified mail. The actual committee meeting lasts for four days and is devoted to building an examination from these questions. Careful consideration is given to the accuracy, wording, difficulty, and suitability of each item as well as the overall scope and balance of the tests. To insure that all questions are within the framework of the official state curriculum, each question is carefully checked against the pertinent paragraphs of the syllabus.
>
> Some idea of the committee's work may be gained from the history of a particular question. When, in 1956, coordinate geometry was mandated in the tenth year course, the committee discussed the need for a few questions which required simple analysis and could not readily be answered graphically. Each member agreed to attempt to compose such questions. In the next mailed interchange appeared:
>
> > Given, a circle with radius of 17 and center at (5, 5). Which of the points, (17, 17), (16, 18), (13, 20) is outside the circle?

The almost universal reaction was "good but too difficult." Various suggestions were made to simplify the problem. One member placed the center
at (0, 0) and tabulated:

Radius	Points
7	(5, 5)
8	(4, 7)
9	(4, 8)
12	(8, 9)
13	(7, 11) (5, 12)
17	(12, 12) (11, 13) (8, 15)

At the committee meeting it was decided to put the center at the origin,
use the smallest set of numbers and require only one computation. The
question, as it finally appeared on the January, 1959, examination, was:

A circle whose radius is 7 has its center at the origin. The point
(5, 5) is:
(a) outside the circle. (b) on the circle. (c) inside the circle.

After this committee's work is completed, the tests are carefully reviewed
by other teacher consultants, by the mathematics supervisor and his three
associates, by testing specialists, and by departmental editors. They are then
duplicated in a form as nearly final as possible and submitted to a revision
committee of school administrators for final approval. Keys to the tests are
then prepared by the departmental staff and the examinations are ready
for the printer. Every step in the preparation is carried out under conditions
of maximum security.

In constructing examinations, many teachers at the local school level
use item construction principles such as described above and advocated
in Chapter 5. But practical problems of administration can give rise to
particular item construction procedures in local situations. Frederick
W. Drewes, Head of the Mathematics Department of Central High,
Trenton, New Jersey, describes a technique developed at his school:

A workable system of tests should have the following features:
1. The tests should be easy to administer and to score.
2. The tests should be available to all teachers of the same subject.
3. Problems of absenteeism should be covered.

The above criteria can be met by a system of mimeographed tests where
a blank or blanks are left in each question. Thus, if we have the equations:

$$3x + 2y = 5$$
$$2x + 5y = (\quad),$$

we can insert different numbers in the blank space. By working out different
sets of values we can use the same test different periods, give different values

to the alternate rows, use another set for an absentee. Criticism of teachers' tests will be at a minimum and achievement can be measured fairly. Slight differences in difficulty due to the numbers inserted in the blanks will usually level out over a complete test if proper thought is used in selecting values.

In slow classes where a few of the pupils are more capable than the others, the pupils can work at their own speed, do their specified assignments, and take their test when they are ready for it, using their assigned values.

Here are some more sample items:

1. In the equation (   ), what is (a) the sum of the roots, (b) the product of the roots?   (a)————————
                                         (b)————————
2. Write the equation of the line perpendicular to $3x - 2y = 9$ that passes through the point (   ).   ————————
3. If x is in Q II and $\sin x = ($ $)$, and y is in Q III and $\cos y = -3/5$, find the value of $\tan (x - y)$.   ————————

Diagnostic Tests

One type of test mentioned in Chapter 6 is the diagnostic test. The Modesto Public School System of Modesto, California, has developed an elaborate scheme of diagnostic testing, including production of its own tests. Special Consultant Herman J. Kopp describes this program:

In an attempt to set up a more adequate phase of diagnosis for our 4th, 5th, and 6th grade arithmetic programs, we have been experimenting with a series of tests. These tests encompass the fundamental processes of addition, subtraction, multiplication, and division of whole numbers, as well as common and decimal fractions.

Each test covering the four basic processes is characterized by two specific points:

1. Problems dealing with the main difficulties students possibly will encounter in a given process at a given grade level. As an example, the diagnostic division tests cover the following types of problems:

   TYPE I
   Even Facts (without remainder)
   Uneven Facts (with remainder)

   TYPE II
   Even and Uneven Division with Two and Three Digit Answers

   TYPE III
   Two Digit Answers with a Terminal Zero, Even and Uneven
   Three Digit Answers with a Terminal Zero, Even and Uneven
   Three Digit Answers with Two Terminal Zeros, Even and Uneven
   Three Digit Answers, Internal Zero, Even and Uneven

Type IV

> Two Digit Divisor—All Types, No Quotient Correction (1, 2, and 3 digit answers), Even and Uneven
>
> Two Digit Divisor—All Types, Quotient Correction (1, 2, and 3 digit answers), Even and Uneven

2. Sufficient problems of each type (at least three) to give an accurate indication to the teacher that a student has mastered the type, or is having difficulties with it. For example, the following division problems for the 5th and 6th grades are taken from TYPE III—Three Digit Answers with Two Terminal Zeros, Even and Uneven:

$$7)\overline{2,800} \qquad\qquad 4)\overline{803} \qquad\qquad 9)\overline{905}$$

Our teachers have used the tests in one of two ways, depending upon the grade level, the ability of the group being taught, and the situation or area of instruction.

1. Teachers apply the tests to diagnose if students have retained a degree of mastery of mathematical skills previously covered.
2. Teachers apply the tests to diagnose what categories within a given type require additional emphasis before the degree of mastery desired can be obtained.

These diagnostic tests help teachers discover whether learning has taken place, the efficiency of performance, the difficulties individuals are having, and the possibilities of grouping for reteaching. Basically, these are teaching tools designed to assist—not to determine a student grade.

Diagnostic Check Lists

There are other kinds of evaluation instruments besides tests (in the ordinary sense), and all kinds of behavior to be measured. Such matters were considered in Chapter 7. W. J. Hegstrom of Delray Beach Junior High School, Delray Beach, Florida, describes his use of a check list for diagnosis of achievement difficulties:

A perceptive teacher is apt to discover, early in his teaching career, the meaning of individual differences in student ability and preparation. He may further note that he can't tell precisely which students have what skills. Diagnostic tests may not be considered usable, and a teacher is prone to forget in 24 hours what problems "Johnny" missed. Obviously, under conditions like these, individual help is apt to be haphazard.

One solution to this problem is a list of skills placed in orderly sequence, and checked as the student progresses. Making such a list is not difficult. The basis can be found in the table of contents of any good eighth grade text. The resulting diagnostic check list not only encourages objectivity in keeping close touch with each student's progress, but also serves as a motivational tool through self-competition.

Table 5 is an excerpt of the check list used at Delray Beach Junior High; this list was printed horizontally over a vertical roster of the class. This served as a class record. A copy of the complete list was given each pupil.

TABLE 5

AN EXCERPT FROM A DIAGNOSTIC CHECK LIST, DELRAY BEACH, FLORIDA

1. Counts with whole numbers to trillions.
   :
4. Knows the meaning and spelling of key words.
   :
6. Uses four processes with fractions.
7. Understands ratio.
   :
11. Finds a percent of a number.
   :
16. Knows measure equivalents.
   :
19. Understands the meaning of *perimeter*, *area*, and *volume*.
20. Uses formulae in finding perimeter of square, rectangle, circle.

Short five-to-ten-item diagnostic quizzes were then administered at close periods of time. These quizzes were most often practice pages of another text. In repeated use it has been found best not to let these quizzes cover more than one item of the list, except in the case of retesting. Retesting was done following the usual remedial methods given those who failed the diagnostic quizzes.

Surprisingly, conscientiousness improved in doing remedial work. This may have been the result of student insight, deflation of overconfidence and/or enlightenment concerning the value of practice. At any rate, evidence of motivation was present. The list provides a vehicle for self-competition and acts as a motivational tool. It destroys a false sense of confidence and provides a sense of satisfaction to those who progress. It gives the teacher and student an objective look at the student's progress.

Records and Reports in Guidance

To implement testing results properly requires an effective guidance program which employs an efficient system of records and reports. In Chapter 9, Theodore E. Kellogg explores the theoretical aspects of this area. Margaret Joseph, Chairman of the Mathematics Department at Shorewood High School, Milwaukee, Wisconsin, provides this description of techniques used at her school:

At the close of each semester, each mathematics teacher records on a printed card, especially designed for that purpose, the semester grade and the results of any standardized test given. He also rates each student's work habits and what he believes to be the student's chances of success in subsequent courses in mathematics. This cumulative record card has space for junior high data on one side and senior high on the other. The information enables one to tell at a glance whether the student is working to capacity.

At the beginning of the second semester, every counselor in grades 8 through 11 is given a form on which he lists in alphabetical order the name of each advisee who wishes to take mathematics the following September. The writer uses the department cards to check all names on these reports. If the card shows good grades in previous and present mathematics courses, good work habits, and a good score on the standardized tests, the choice of subject is approved without consulting other teachers in the department. A memorandum is made of students who have at least a 3.5 average in mathematics, for they are candidates for the accelerated section. If the card shows low C or D grades and poor work habits, then the student's permanent record folder is consulted to discover other significant data. This might include grades earned in other courses, the Cooperative English Test score, rank in the statewide test, and any other pertinent information. For example, if a student wants to take geometry, but most of his grades are D's and his rating on the Cooperative English Test is at the 20th percentile, he would be advised either to take no more high school mathematics or to enroll in a modified course in geometry. (There is a high correlation between success in English comprehension and ability to succeed in geometry.) If some grades are low, but others not, then his present mathematics teacher is consulted to help make the decision.

When all cases listed on the report from the counselors have been thoroughly checked and a decision reached, a new report is typed to inform the counselor of this decision. This report is used by the counselor when the students fill out program cards in spring for the following September. Not only does each counselor receive a report for his advisees, but a complete report is given to each of the deans and one is kept in the files of the mathematics department. In September this report is used by the teachers of high school mathematics. Each checks his class lists with the report to see that all students are enrolled in the proper section. If a pupil is enrolled in a class where he does not belong, he is sent to the dean for a correction in his program. New names are listed and checked. We have many new students who come from other schools; their grades are checked as soon as their transcript of credits is received.

Administration of an Evaluation Program

Miss Joseph's statement provides an illustration of how a mathematics department in an individual high school may serve a guidance and reporting function. In contrast to this, in many of the larger United States school systems specially trained supervisory personnel have been hired and centralized departments organized in order to handle the extensive procedures associated with evaluation in all schools and in all school subjects. Gary, Indiana, has such an organization, as described by Supervisor of Testing Paul A. Melchert:

The city-wide standardized testing program is directed by the Research Department. The mechanics of the program, *viz.*, ordering, scheduling, distributing, collecting, and scoring, are major responsibilities of the Department. After the tests have been machine-scored, the raw data are transferred to punch cards for further processing by the I.B.M. department. The final interpretive data are prepared in report form, called "data sheets." Information derived from the testing program is used for evaluation, prediction, and research, as follows:

1. Data sheets contain the symbolic characteristics of the students and the groups with which the students are compared. The descriptive information provided in the data sheets consists of: names, chronological ages, scores, means, medians, standard deviations, and standard errors of measurement. Copies of the data sheets are sent to teachers, counselors, principals, and supervisors. One of the greatest values of the testing program lies in *the manner in which the test scores are presented to the student for his use.* He may acquire better self-understanding by utilizing the symbols provided him.
2. Summary reports, prepared for the superintendents, contain histograms based upon the scores made by each school on the various tests. Included with the histograms are medians, means, and standard deviations of national, city, and school populations.
3. Local norms are established for achievement tests, and are periodically revised. These norms are prepared in booklet form and distributed to all counselors for use in student counseling.
4. Local course objectives may not coincide with the objectives measured by nationally distributed tests. The achievement tests, therefore, are item analyzed for evaluation. The analyses are submitted to administrative and supervisory personnel for use with faculty groups in curriculum planning.
5. Simple prediction and follow-up studies are prepared for counselors who assist students in educational planning. These studies consist of scatter-diagrams and expectancy tables based upon criterion measures and test scores.

As may be inferred from the above, at regularly scheduled times of the year the Gary, Indiana, school system administers a variety of mathematics tests to all pupils in all elementary and high schools. The Penn Hills School District of Pittsburgh, Pennsylvania, has an equally extensive testing program in mathematics, but uses a somewhat different organizational technique. This is described below by Director of Secondary Education Arthur C. Kelley. Note also Dr. Kelley's references to the ninth grade algebra versus general mathematics decision, and to reports to parents.

In the elementary schools, standardized tests given to all pupils in a particular grade are administered and scored by self-contained-classroom teachers who are responsible for the major portion of the curriculum. The Director of Elementary Education coordinates this testing effort, summarizing scores and interpreting results to patrons and the professional staff. Tests administered to selected pupils for whom more information is desired are given directly by the Director of Elementary Education.

In the secondary schools, general achievement and mental ability type tests are administered by homeroom teachers and scored cooperatively. Specialized mathematics tests, such as prognostic, aptitude, or specific achievement instruments of the kind that might be employed in algebra or geometry, are administered by mathematics teachers. The entire testing program in the secondary division is coordinated, interpreted, and statistically summarized by the Director of Guidance and the Director of Secondary Education. In this way, individual and group data involving strengths and weaknesses in mathematics are immediately available to teachers who have instructional responsibilities in mathematics, while at the same time the entire testing pattern is integrated to aid in the solution of any problems that might be identified by total pupil performance.

Obviously, a great deal of teacher time and effort is necessary to promote such a comprehensive evaluation program. But counseling pupils and planning learning opportunities are important elements in the professional roles teachers are called upon to fulfill in a comprehensive curriculum. Establishing an equity in the testing program through broad participation is a legitimate professional way of realizing these basic teaching functions.

Complete records of standardized test performance in mathematics are kept in each student's cumulative record folder. These records include special profile sheets listing specific test results, as well as summarized anecdotal data, so that trends revealed from several tests in mathematics can be identified. This information is very important to teachers at every level of a child's progress through school.

And this data is particularly important in the junior and senior high schools where every student is called upon to make increasingly specific decisions about his post-high-school plans. Our eighth and ninth grade mathematics teachers make significant contributions to the guidance program by recommending students for advanced mathematics study. These recommendations are made on the basis of class performance and school marks as well as capabilities revealed from standardized instruments. Because of the broad testing program, every pupil's capabilities and interests in mathematics can be assessed, both in relationship with national norms and with standards that have been established in the local district. We have found, for example, that eighth grade pupils who fall very much below a critical score of 40 on the Orleans Algebra Prognosis Test, and who have a grade achievement of 8.3 or less in mathematics skills on the Iowa Tests, have a very difficult time in algebra in the ninth grade and should, if their interest is sustained, postpone Algebra I, in favor of General Mathematics, until the tenth grade.

Results of standardized tests are shared broadly with parents and pupils in Penn Hills. Typical of the way this is accomplished is the extract in Table 6 from the junior high school report card which is distributed every nine weeks:

TABLE 6

EXTRACT FROM JUNIOR HIGH SCHOOL REPORT CARD
PENN HILLS SCHOOL DISTRICT, PITTSBURGH, PENNSYLVANIA

RECORD OF STANDARDIZED TESTS					
The results indicated under this section are based on examinations which the School District buys from national testing organizations. Your child's rating on standardized tests listed below is compared to that of thousands of other students of the same age over the United States.					
Types of Tests	High	Above Average	Average	Below Average	Low

Percentile rankings or grade equivalents conforming to the 5-point scale listed on the report card are established. This information is made available through the report card so that personal conferences among parents, teachers, guidance counselors, and administrators can be arranged for further co-operative analysis. Although there are many arguments in professional literature for and against making known students' general performance on standardized tests, we believe there are many advantages, not the least of which is the fact that parents can profit from an evaluative judgment in addition to that of the teacher alone.

Prediction of Success in High School Mathematics

The Des Moines Independent Community School District of Iowa also has an extensive evaluation program. A portion of that program is concerned with prediction of success in high school mathematics courses.

Howard Blanchard, Director, Department of Guidance, Educational Research and Testing, describes the program in this way:

The mathematics testing program consists of one achievement test given per year in grades 3, 4, 5, 7, and 8. There are reading tests given at each of these grade levels. The reading test scores are most valuable when attempts are made to predict success in mathematics courses.

The Iowa Algebra Aptitude Test is given to two groups of students. One group consists of second semester seventh grade students who are recommended as understanding the basic mathematics concepts normally taught through grade eight. Several of these students will take algebra as an eighth grade subject. Also, all second semester eighth graders take this aptitude test.

In Des Moines, the Iowa Algebra Aptitude Test scores indicate predictive chances for above average grades in algebra ranging from four chances out of five when the test percentile rank is 93 or above, to one chance out of eight when the test percentile is 0 to 7. Table 7 exhibits complete results for algebra aptitude test administrations over a ten year period.

TABLE 7

IOWA ALGEBRA APTITUDE TEST SCORES VERSUS ALGEBRA GRADES
TEN YEARS EXPERIENCE WITH 8,273 STUDENTS WHO ELECTED ALGEBRA
DES MOINES, IOWA, SCHOOLS

Test Percentile Rank		Grade Distribution
93+	A	46%
	B	33%
	C	17%
	D	3%
	F	1%
70-92	A	20%
	B	33%
	C	33%
	D	12%
	F	2%
31-69	A	7%
	B	23%
	C	41%
	D	26%
	F	3%
8-30	A	4%
	B	16%
	C	34%
	D	40%
	F	6%
0-7	A	4%
	B	8%
	C	42%
	D	42%
	F	4%

The Iowa Plane Geometry Aptitude Test has been given to students who are interested in electing geometry as one of their courses. In Des Moines, these test scores indicate predictive chances for above average grades in geometry ranging from ten out of ten when the test percentile rank is 93 or above, to zero out of ten when the percentile rank is 0 to 7.

Similar predictive results have been obtained from American Council Psychological Examination scores and arithmetic average grades. In the future, predictive results will be figured from scores on the School and College Ability Tests; these have now replaced the American Council Psychological Examination test administration in grades nine and eleven.

The research in the local school system reveals the best predictive tools for that school system. Generally, the better the test scores, the better the chances for making above average grades in a specific mathematics course.

Evaluation of Curriculum Development

Evaluation is, of course, fundamental to research. At present, national attention in mathematics education research is focused upon curriculum development, particularly at the secondary level. In Minnesota, the Mathematics Division of the Minnesota National Laboratory has started extensive experimentation with such materials as those developed by the School Mathematics Study Group. The purpose of the Laboratory is not to recommend materials for adoption. It will conduct experiments and publish its results, on the basis of which school people may draw their own conclusions. Paul C. Rosenbloom, Director of that Laboratory, illustrates some methods of curriculum evaluation in this report of some research in the Minnesota project:

The Minnesota National Laboratory is an agency of the Minnesota State Department of Education, which has the purpose of conducting scientific experimentation and evaluation of new curricular materials. A description of the Laboratory is contained in Newsletter No. 2 of the School Mathematics Study Group. We shall sketch some evaluation work done by the Laboratory under contract with the School Mathematics Study Group (SMSG).

During the academic year 1958-59, the Laboratory conducted a dry run of the SMSG experimental units for grades 7-8, and a preliminary comparison between the Course I of the University of Illinois Committee on School Mathematics and the conventional 9th grade courses.

In the latter experiment there were four teachers, each teaching one experimental and one control class, and ten teachers, approximately as well qualified as the other four, teaching only control classes in separated schools. The classes were comparable in aptitude as measured by the Differential Aptitude Tests. We measured achievement by both the Cooperative Elementary and Intermediate Algebra Tests and the Illinois Test of Basic

Mathematical Concepts, and gave retention tests the following September. We made comparisons both for whole classes and for ability levels within classes. The experiment was replicated on a somewhat larger scale during the academic year 1959-60. New instruments were constructed to obtain a better measure of achievement.

In the SMSG experiment we had 1 sixth grade class, 17 seventh grade classes, and 7 eighth grade classes, some homogeneously and some heterogeneously grouped. We tested all classes with School and College Ability Tests for aptitude and Sequential Tests of Educational Progress for achievement on the conventional content, and the writing team of the Minnesota School Mathematics Center constructed unit tests for achievement on the new content. The latter tests were item-analyzed and revised for the academic year 1959-60. We computed regressions of achievement versus aptitude, and of achievement versus teacher qualifications measured in terms of experience, grades in undergraduate and graduate mathematics courses, activities in professional mathematical organizations, and contributions to the advancement of mathematical education.

During the academic year 1959-60 the Laboratory conducted comparison experiments between SMSG and conventional seventh grade courses, Illinois and conventional ninth grade courses, dry runs on SMSG sample texts in grades 8-12, and a pilot study of the SMSG seventh grade courses in 7 sixth grade classes. We also conducted a pilot study of the use of the SMSG ninth and tenth grade texts, supplemented by material written by Professor A. B. Willcox of Amherst College and P. C. Rosenbloom especially for gifted students, in a correspondence course aimed at the top ½ of 1 percent of the ninth and tenth graders in Minnesota, Wisconsin, Iowa, and the Dakotas. About 130 teachers participated in this 1959-60 program.

In the space allotted here, it would be impossible to report fairly the results of these experiments. But the Minnesota National Laboratory will publish technical reports containing enough of the raw data so that independent investigators may check the results. As these reports become available, their publication will be announced in *The Mathematics Teacher*.

As Dr. Rosenbloom has just pointed out, it is often advantageous to write new achievement tests for the evaluation of curriculum research. Emil Berger of St. Paul, Minnesota, has provided the following description of a project in writing and analyzing especially designed unit tests for the evaluation of eleventh grade School Mathematics Study Group material.

The eight teachers of experimental material meet every second Saturday. At these sessions the mathematics involved is discussed by a mathematician. Discussions are also held regarding the teaching of the material and the important ideas to be tested.

Following this seminar discussion, the teachers write test items that they consider useful. These items are then submitted to a mathematics educator who selects items, writes new items, and makes up a test that samples the important goals of a given unit. The items are then submitted to a mathematician for a further check. Finally, the director edits the items for correctness of form, grammar, and organization. The tests are then duplicated and distributed to the teachers of experimental classes.

Test data from these experimental classes are collected and tabulated to give information for an item analysis of the tests. This item analysis indicates the difficulty level of the items, the discriminatory power, and the level of achievement of classes and individual students. The reactions of teachers to these tests and to individual items are recorded. On the basis of this information the tests are revised so that a reliable and valid test will result.

This test writing project has been a valuable experience to everyone involved and has resulted in some excellent unit tests.

Implications

The 18 descriptions above clearly indicate that good evaluation techniques are being used in some American public schools. What are their implications? First, each reader will undoubtedly want to re-examine these models to determine whether his school is doing all it should in evaluation of its mathematics instruction. In doing so, he should look for strengths in his school's program. And as these are noted, it is to be hoped that he will report them to a professional journal so that others may benefit. But he will surely look also for weaknesses, and if he finds any, he may use the evaluation practices in this chapter as models for improvement. Other chapters in this book will provide further guides.

But there are implications of a more national character. In the process of finding good evaluation techniques which merited description in this chapter, we had hints that good local evaluation programs may exist to a lesser extent than necessary or desirable. The first hint of this arose when four of the responding state departments and one of the national authorities were unable to identify outstanding school testing programs in mathematics. In fact, one state department representative asserted: "We do not have . . . any school systems that have outstanding testing programs in the area of mathematics." The other four replies may be summarized in the words of one: "I know of none in this state to fit your needs."

Do these states really lack good mathematics evaluation programs? If so, are there other states where the same condition exists? Fourteen states did not respond at all to the request for identification of outstanding programs. Of course these state departments may have been overly critical or poorly informed. But further indications of weakness may be inferred from the fact that more than 40 percent of 115 recommended schools did not respond to the request for outlines of their evaluation programs. Such suspicions received further support late in the selection process by the failure of two-fifths of even the finally selected 35 schools to supply statements for publication.

These suspicions may be more fanciful than real, possibly brought about by the nature of the survey or the perceptions of the observer. But this hypothesis is worthy of test: Fewer schools in the United States have quality testing programs than should be the case in terms of the present state of theoretical knowledge.

Clearly this survey did not intend to test such a conjecture. Certainly, good evaluation techniques are in use, as the previous section testifies. But the hypothesis is an important one. With National Defense Education Act funds being used to improve mathematics instruction and evaluation programs, the matter should certainly be resolved.

Summary

The purpose of this chapter has been to answer the question: "In what ways are some schools actually using recommended techniques from the theory of evaluation in mathematics instruction?"

An answer was provided through brief descriptions of specific practices used by 18 schools or school systems in 14 states. Representatives from these schools wrote the descriptions; contextual remarks were made by the author. The schools were discovered and selected by the use of a national survey.

The descriptions illustrate the following evaluation techniques:
1. Selection of students for accelerated classes
2. Guidance for ninth grade mathematics
3. Test selection
4. Test construction
5. Item construction
6. Diagnostic tests
7. Diagnostic check lists
8. Records and reports in guidance
9. Administration of an evaluation program
10. Prediction of success in high school mathematics
11. Evaluation of curriculum development.

Despite the possibility of errors of omission and commission, it is hoped that this chapter has provided models which other teachers, schools, and school systems may imitate, revise, and/or improve.

9

Recording, Reporting, and Interpreting Records

THEODORE E. KELLOGG

AFTER objectives are stated, evaluation techniques and procedures chosen, instruments of evaluation administered, and data collected, the vast store of information must be recorded and organized for a variety of uses. Mathematics teachers must be concerned with the nature and purpose of records, adequacy of classroom and departmental records, principles of marking and reporting, implications for marking of ability grouping, the meaning of standards, appropriate ways of combining scores, the use of profiles, and the possibilities of machine recording. Basic to all recording and reporting is the need for adequate communication and interpretation of information. This chapter discusses such matters by outlining principles and providing illustrations.

The Nature and Purpose of Records

The basic purpose of records, whether they are for faculty, parents, employers, or students, is communication. Several types and levels of communication are outlined in Table 1.

Communication of mathematics attainment is usually written, and usually involves symbolizing a sample of total behavior at a point in time removed from the occurance of the behavior. Thus records must be self-descriptive, precise, and representative of total behavior. Oral clarification is often not possible and original behavior cannot be repeated for the purpose of improving observation, selection and evaluation.

As suggested by Table 1, records of performance in mathematics are multipurpose in character. A recorded test score, for example, may be referred to by the teacher in assigning grades, or it may be interpreted to parents, or it may provide the basis for research. Therefore, in choosing what is to be recorded many uses must be kept in mind. Sometimes the same information must be recorded in different ways to be useful.

TABLE 1

LEVELS AND TYPES OF EVALUATIVE COMMUNICATION IN MATHEMATICS

Classroom, School, and Community Behavior Relating
to Attainment in Mathematics
|
Summarize and Record
(Grades, Scores, Check Lists, Ratings, Comments)
|

Class Records	Department or Grade Records	School Records

Summarize and Report
(Report Cards, Applications, Grades, Scores, Check Lists, Ratings, Comments)
|

Schools	Students	Parents	Employers	Researchers	Colleges

Since recorded information is often a distillation of large amounts of raw data, we must maintain information about the nature of original sources and collection techniques. In many cases original sources need to be preserved, since they may be needed at a later date for checking accuracy of records or for obtaining types of information not included in summaries. For example, original data may be needed to check a particular student's tendency to commit a certain type of computational or reasoning error. It is essential also to maintain sample copies of tests used. These may be extremely important in self-evaluation by the teacher or in determining the content achievement symbolized by a score or a class average.

Records must be readily available for use by appropriate persons. Teachers must have access to departmental records at any time and over extended periods of time. Many research studies have not materialized because needed data, even though recorded, was not readily available in usable form. The mathematics teacher may have collected information of interest to an employer or to a college, but if the task of transferring the information is unreasonably burdensome, it may never be used.

These comments provide a brief account of the many and sometimes complex decisions that must be made if information is to be recorded so that it will be used. It is important to note that these decisions must be made for the mathematics evaluation program as a whole because of the interrelationships among all aspects. Thus advance planning is necessary, since it is difficult, if not impossible, to develop an acceptable coordinated mathematics record program by meeting each specific need as it develops.

A final comment should be made about the practicability of mathematical performance record keeping as it will be discussed here. There can be little doubt of the importance of class records, cumulative departmental or subject records, summary test distributions, and report cards. It is true that the number of pupils and the added responsibilities the teacher has come to accept may make the keeping of adequate evaluation records a burdensome and extremely difficult accomplishment.

It seems clear, however, that whatever responsibilities the teacher may need to dismiss, evaluation and adequate record keeping must not be among them. The demands upon the time of mathematics teachers undoubtedly will force many compromises in the amount and quality of information that can be collected and recorded. In many cases it is imperative that clerical help be available to assist teachers in record keeping if they are to meet their complex teaching responsibilities. However, the central position of evaluation and the necessity for meaningful recording of evaluative information inevitably make these matters a responsibility of the mathematics teacher.

Classroom Records

The mathematics classroom situation provides the basis for day to day sampling of student behavior. Following are some types of information that may be recorded by the classroom teacher:

1. Assignment results
2. Attendance
3. Scores on quizzes and examinations
4. Anecdotal comments
5. Evaluation of projects, reports, demonstrations
6. Frequency and quality of recitation
7. Classroom citizenship.

The variety of information to be recorded suggests that the grade book will be of partial value. The typical grade book is usually adequate for attendance records, checking assignments, and recording quizzes. It is apparent, however, that project evaluation, quality of recitation, and anecdotal comments may need to be recorded in some other way— perhaps in a folder developed for each student.

The classroom record is a primary source of mathematics performance data, and it is important to keep such records up to date. Since significant events are likely to occur each day—at least for some students—it may be wise to set aside time each day for current recording in addition to the recording that occurs during the classroom situation. The classroom record, like all other records, should be complete and self-contained. If coding is used in the grade book, it may be desirable to summarize the coding system in the grade book itself so that the meanings of symbols will be readily available. The information to be included in the grade book and student folder should be planned in advance and the recording document organized and sectioned accordingly for recording of like information in a single section or location.

If a folder is used, a format may be printed inside it, or a printed information sheet may be enclosed for summary purposes (see section on departmental records). The folder should contain work samples and anecdotal comments. All information recorded should be dated and signed for future reference. The individual student folder should be passed from teacher to teacher, becoming one part of the departmental record. The grade book may be retained by the individual teacher or it may be filed, as required.

Cumulative Records and Departmental Records

Although central comprehensive school records are essential, departmental records are also important for an adequate evaluation program. Department or subject area records permit the recording of far more detailed and comprehensive information than is reasonable or possible in over-all school records. Such information is also more accessible to the teacher.

In discussing the classroom record we recommended a student record folder in addition to the regular grade book. While the grade book is the individual teachers' day-to-day record, the folder provides the basis for a departmental record which may be passed on from year to year. Work samples, anecdotal comments, and in some cases completed tests are placed in the folder during the school year. At the end of each school year, or at other appropriate intervals, information from the grade book and from the folder should be summarized and condensed to permit maximum usability. This summary may be made on a printed form inside the folder itself or it may be made on a departmental card to be filed in the folder or in a separate alphabetical file. The cumulative departmental record summary is a distillation of information from the grade book and of anecdotal materials and student work. The following items illustrate what this summary could include:

1. Achievement test scores
2. Diagnostic test scores
3. Aptitude test scores
4. Behavior patterns suggested by anecdotal records
5. Areas of strength, difficulty, or weakness
6. Classes taken and grades earned.

Table 2 illustrates a format for summarizing departmental or elementary school information pertaining to mathematics performance. A similar form would be required for grades 8 through 12. Modifications would be necessary, of course, for specific situations. As the form is presented, it might be printed on the front and back of a heavy card or on the two inner sides of a file folder. Grade levels and names of standard tests may be printed on the summary form.

For illustrative purposes several sample entries have been made on the record card in Table 2. The section on test information gives the form of each test along with the exact date and grade of administration. The number of raw score points possible is given along with the student's raw score. Raw scores are useful for many research purposes. Several types of derived scores are reported and specifically labeled, such as percentile rank; grade score; standard score with $\overline{x} = 50$, s.d. $= 15$; and IQ with standard error of measurement.

Percentile ranks have the advantage of providing ready comparison with other members of the normative group, but they are not additive and therefore have limited research value. Grade scores, although seemingly easy to interpret, are not subject to arithmetic manipulation, and they tend to mask variability. Particular grade scores are often assigned by interpolation or extrapolation, and as a result considerable error may be introduced. They are based on a somewhat artificial classification that may vary considerably from school to school, and they may imply standards that create unrealistic expectations for less able students and unrealistic satisfaction with the performance of more able students. Similar problems, perhaps in lesser degree, occur with other types of scores. Age scores are essentially analagous to grade scores.

TABLE 2

ILLUSTRATIVE MATHEMATICS RECORD CARD

Underwood	Barbara	3/8/50	AD 4-0000
Last Name	First	Birth Date	Telephone

194 Belmont Road	Housewife	Engineer
Address	Mother's Occupation	Father's Occupation

A. Test Information

Name of Test	Date Taken	Grade	Raw Score/ Possible Score	Derived Score	Norm Group	Comments
TTTT Form Q	3/16/60	5	80/110	Percentile rank = 65	5th graders in "X" school March '60	50 percentile = 70 $\bar{x}=60$ s.d. = 10
ZZZ Form A	10/10/60	6	56/85	Grade score = 7.8	Extrapolation from national sample, 5th & 6th grades	6th grade: $\bar{x}=40$ s.d. = 15
XXXX Form X	10/15/61	7	90/150	SS = 65 ($\bar{x}=50$, s.d. = 15)	Publishers national sample 7th grade	$\bar{x}=80$ ⎱ Natl. s.d. = 10 ⎰ Sample
YYY Form B	11/10/61	7	180/250	IQ = 120 ±6	Publishers national sample 7th grade	$\bar{x}=100$ ⎱ Natl. s.d. = 15 ⎰ Sample

B. Anecdotal and Evaluative Comments (indicate teacher, grade, date)

Gave excellent report on area of geometric figures.   Miss B. 6th grade, 10/12/60.
Has been openly critical of errors made by classmates for several months and as a result is not well accepted by her peers.   Mr. R. 2/5/62.

C. Marks Earned

Grade	Mark	Comment	Grade	Mark	Comment
Kinder-garten	Satis.	Good number sense A.B. 6/ 55	4		
1			5		
2			6		
3			7	B	Compared with other 7th graders in her class (C.D. 6/61)

Standard scores have many advantages. They may have a common mean and standard deviation. When raw scores are changed to standard scores, equality of units is obtained, and the standard scores are additive. The change does not modify the shape of the original raw score distribution. In dealing with equivalent or analogous populations, standard scores may be added and compared meaningfully. It may be desirable, therefore, to consider using this type of derived score for recording all test scores. Very often in attempting to get an over-all assessment of the student at the end of a semester or year the teacher will wish to combine a series of scores. If the raw scores on each test have been converted to standard scores, the teacher may simply average the scores. To weight a particular standard score more heavily, it may be doubled or tripled in arriving at the average. Such arithmetic manipulation may not be performed with percentile ranks or raw scores. Raw scores may also be converted to derived scores that take a desired form such as the normal probability curve. Such conversion has value for certain research situations. The last type of derived score illustrated in Table 2 is the IQ. The standard error of measurement shows the range within which the true score on the particular test probably lies (specific probability levels may be determined).

Although the description of normative groups in Table 2 is brief, grade level and general population are indicated. Normative group description is essential, since no score has meaning by itself. The indication "publisher's national sample" suggests the need for referring to the test manual for additional information. For test "ZZZ" the table shows that the grade score was obtained by extrapolation from a fifth and sixth grade sample. Thus although a grade score of 7.8 is given the test was not administered to seventh graders. In several instances additional information is provided under the heading *Comments*.

Anecdotal comments in Table 2 briefly report significant behavior with emphasis on factual information. The date of recording and the name of the teacher are given. Under *Marks Earned* the general meaning of the mark recorded should be self-evident, and a statement giving the basis for it should be provided, since many marking systems are in use.

The information provided by Table 2 is minimal for adequate communication. When information is recorded it must be remembered that the report will be used by other persons, possibly several years later. Details that appear obvious at the time of recording may not seem obvious to a different teacher at a later time.

Another phase of departmental records is the keeping of group test data for important mathematics tests. In order that tests, teaching, and departmental development may be studied and evaluated, a central departmental or subject file of test results should be maintained. Such a file should contain distribution of test scores by class, grade, and teacher, as appropriate. A sample test should be attached to each set of distributions and each score distribution should be carefully labeled and dated. All important mathematics tests should be included, as well as some general ability tests. Raw scores and appropriate derived scores should be recorded. It should be possible to associate student names with particular distributions if that proves necessary. Record keeping is simplified if a form is mimeographed for tabulation.

Some special comment may be made about the elementary school program. Since arithmetic is only one of many subjects for which the elementary teacher is responsible, day-to-day record keeping may involve the coordination of many subject areas. The principles and practices for recording arithmetic achievement, however, are basically the same as those applying to mathematics. Although the grade book and the cumulative record folder may involve a variety of subjects, those portions related to arithmetic performance should follow the general patterns thus far discussed. It is extremely important that distinct records of arithmetic achievement be kept. Perhaps it would be more appropriate to think of a subject area (arithmetic) record than a departmental record at the elementary school level. In any case, cumulative records of arithmetic performance should pass from grade to grade and from teacher to teacher.

Marking Systems and Report Cards

The report card provides a fundamental communication link from the teacher to students and their parents. Since types of marking systems and report cards are so varied, the value of a summary seems questionable. We should be concerned instead with basic principles and purposes; specific notations and procedures are the responsibility of the particular school, teacher, or department. The following principles are suggested for developing and using marking systems and report cards for mathematics. Their application is illustrated by the sample report form in Table 3, which, of course, would require modification for use in a particular school.

Principles

1. THE NOTATIONS AND REPORT FORMS USED IN MATHEMATICS ARE ARBITRARY; THE MEANING CONVEYED BY THE NOTATION AND FORM IS IMPORTANT. Again the basic purpose of communication must be con-

sidered. It makes little difference whether a mathematics pupil receives a "75," a "C," an "S," or a "G." What does make a difference is the meaning the symbol suggests to the person reading it. A new symbol for each modification in meaning is probably not needed. It is only necessary that the meaning of the symbol be unambiguous. Perhaps the most urgent need, then, is not that we all adopt the same symbols (which is most unlikely), but that we carefully define the symbols we decide to use.

In the illustrative report form shown in Table 3 the only letter or number symbol used is the final mark notation. A final over-all grade is extremely useful. Brief words and phrases are used in the remaining evaluations. Terms such as *average* and *upper half* have self-evident meaning in relation to an objective and a comparison base. A numerical or letter symbol could supplement these phrases, but such symbols would require additional definition.

2. THE MARKING AND REPORTING TECHNIQUES MUST BE SUCH THAT THE TEACHER MAY USE THEM WITHOUT MAKING UNWARRANTED IN- FERENCES, ASSUMPTIONS, AND EXTRAPOLATIONS. In some instances the detail and the basic nature of the reporting system or the marking system are such that the teacher has a choice between appearing to know little about the student and making evaluations that appear im- pressive but are based on little objective observation or evidence. However desirable it may be to evaluate a student in a certain area, it is unwise to attempt this in the absence of systematic information. For example, no attempt should be made to evaluate a student's appre- ciation of mathematics if supporting evidence is not available. To com- pare what a student does with what he should be able to do, one must have evidence that suggests what a person with this student's characteris- tics should be able to do. Evaluation based on suppositions may be harmful to the student.

3. THE MARKING AND REPORTING TECHNIQUES SHOULD BE AS SIMPLE AS THE NATURE OF THE INFORMATION TO BE CONVEYED PERMITS. Some methods of assigning mathematics grades are quite complex. Some methods of evaluation require lengthy reporting. The teacher should choose techniques of mark assignment and reporting that are as brief and explicit as possible. This permits use of the techniques within the teacher's time limitations and it increases the probability that the person receiving the evaluation will understand it.

4. THE REPORT CARD SHOULD BE SELF-DESCRIPTIVE. Information used in assigning and reporting marks should be clearly stated. This

TABLE 3

ILLUSTRATIVE STUDENT REPORT FORM FOR MATHEMATICS

Semester: Fall Winter 19___   Name   Phillips   Bonita
                                                       Last   First

Algebra I | |
Subject   Honor Section   Regular Section

Student Behavior	COMPARISON BASE				Comments
	Potential Ability	Other Class Members	National Sample	College Entrants	
Skill in Fundamental Computations	Average	Average	Upper Half	Average	
Ability to Read New Material with Understanding	———	———	Average	Below Average	
Over-all Knowledge of Basic Factual Information	Adequate	Fair	Average	———	
Ability to Recognize Relationships and Make Quantitative Inferences	Average	Below Average	Below Average	Below Average	
Participation in Class Discussion	———	Adequate	———	———	
Study Habits	———	Fair	———	Poor	Does not use study time well.
Over-all Achievement on Standardized Tests	———	Average	Average	———	

Mark _____ _____   (Achievement in this class as compared with other
      Semester   Final   class members and adequate performance in the
_____   subject matter—A for excellent, B, C, D, and U for
          Instructor   unsatisfactory.)

Comments: _____

_____

_____

_____

_____

definition is necessary if the teacher is to assign grades objectively and the parent, student, or employer is to understand these marks or grades. Three dimensions must be considered in assigning and reporting marks: (*a*) the characteristics (or objectives) to be evaluated, (*b*) the comparison base to be used, (*c*) the degree of the student's deviation with respect to the comparison base, and the symbol used to describe this deviation. Table 3 illustrates the use of such dimensions.

Marks should be related to specific mathematics objectives. A single over-all mark is valuable, but evaluation of the components making up the mark adds needed meaning. Evaluation with respect to specific student behavior helps the teacher to report progress. Student achievement is thus reported in such terms as *ability to solve new problems, ability to read mathematical discussion,* and *ability to retain basic factual information.*

The comparison base indicates the group, individual, or standard with which a student is compared. Every mark is a comparison. *Is the student with a high grade in plane geometry doing well as compared with his potential? as compared with the other geometry students in his class? as compared with geometry students in his state? as compared with a national sample of geometry students? as compared with some defined standard?* All or only some of the suggested comparisons may apply. The mathematics teacher must decide which comparisons can and should be made.

After objectives and comparison bases are selected, it is possible to determine the units or qualitative terms to describe the student's relative position. The teacher may choose derived scores, letter grades, numerical grades, or phrases such as *above average* and *superior.* Some of these possibilities have the advantage of self definition; for example, the meaning of percentile rank with respect to a particular objective and comparison base is reasonably clear. Other possibilities such as letter grades require further definition. Perhaps, as illustrated in Table 3, phrases like *upper half* and *average* are best understood and most representative of the precision possible.

5. THE VALIDITY OF A GRADING AND REPORTING SYSTEM SHOULD BE EXPERIMENTALLY DETERMINED. Some of the bases for assigning and reporting grades are not empirical. We make certain assumptions, and from them certain principles follow. However, if we are to determine the effectiveness of our evaluations we must also approach the problem experimentally. By interview or questionnaire the mathematics teacher should determine whether the reporting system is conveying adequate and accurate information to the parent, the student, and the employer.

Validity is also related to the quality and type of prediction afforded by marks. If grades are to indicate probable success to the employer, the college, and the student himself, it follows that the degree of correspondence between mathematics ratings and later success must be studied. This follow-up procedure is not easy and it takes extended periods of time. However, by collecting data on college grades and job success the mathematics teacher can acquire information about students' achievement in later endeavors with relation to their high school mathematics grades. If such a study is to be fruitful, it should be consistent with sound research procedures. Since many factors contribute to high school students' later success or difficulty, one must seek patterns of information rather than generalize from an individual case.

6. THE MARKING AND REPORTING SYMBOLS SHOULD NOT SUGGEST MORE KNOWLEDGE ABOUT THE STUDENT OR GREATER ACCURACY OF KNOWLEDGE THAN THE PERSON ASSIGNING THE MARK POSSESSES. When the teacher comes to the point of actually assigning a grade or rating he should choose a notation that is only as precise as the supporting evidence. In some cases a descriptive word may be best; for example, *Good* or *Satisfactory;* in others, general classification may be possible; for example, *upper quarter.* If five letter-grades are used it must be possible to differentiate students meaningfully and accurately into five rank order classifications. A major difficulty in assigning a specific number as a grade is that this number often implies considerably more accuracy than the supporting data permit. Furthermore, it may imply a standard that is not clearly defined. The choices among raw scores and various types of derived scores are discussed elsewhere in this yearbook.

The above principles, considered with the illustrations given, should be of assistance in developing an adequate, objective report card. Several other matters deserve additional comment: (*a*) the implications for marking of ability grouping. (*b*) notes to parents and interviews, (*c*) motivation and marking, (*d*) standards.

Ability Grouping

Ability Grouping has many implications for the assignment of marks. (We use the term here to mean grouping by achievement or potential in mathematics.) It should be remembered, however, that grouping is simply a formal organization of individual differences that exist among ungrouped students. Therefore much of the ensuing discussion applies beyond the grouping situation. As shown in Table 3, the report card should offer the teacher an opportunity to indicate the type of group or section in which the student has been placed—for example, regular, honor, or college preparatory.

The variety of comparisons that may be made in evaluating a particular student are illustrated in Table 3. These comparisons permit reporting a student's progress in relation to his own potential, to other members of his class, and to broader external populations. All of these comparisons are needed for adequate communication. For example, a student in a mathematics class may be doing good work in relation to his potential (this is extremely difficult to judge), average work in relation to his classmates, and below average work in relation to college-bound students. This type of evaluation avoids many of the ambiguities of reporting for different types of sections.

The assignment of a single over-all grade in the absence of other information creates difficult reporting problems (and current practice is to record a single grade for a particular class and student in reporting school records to employers and colleges). The report form illustrated in Table 3, which is primarily for the student and parent, provides far more information than single over-all grades.

How shall we report the single grade with maximum meaning? This question must be answered in terms of the uses to which the single grade will be put, such as college admission, determining competence to continue in mathematics, and determining competence to handle jobs requiring mathematics.

The report card shown in Table 3 provides for a single over-all grade in addition to other evaluations. The grade is assigned in relation to two criteria: achievement of other class members and adequate performance in the subject matter. These criteria seem to the author to be the best bases for assigning a single over-all grade. Sometimes achievement of other class members has been used as the only criterion of adequate performance. This assumes that the characteristics of the class members are such that those in the upper "X" percent of the class are doing an adequate job. In some degree this is usually true, but outside criteria are helpful. These may include the teacher's judgment, achievement of students in a national sample, and the ultimate success of students completing the particular class at earlier times. With continued follow-up of students and with curriculum study the term *adequate performance* can be quantified for particular situations. This quantification may develop in terms of scores on standardized tests or scores on tests written by the teacher. At best, however, the teacher will always need to make judgments as to what constitutes adequate performance. This is one of his professional responsibilities. If these suggestions are followed, the over-all grade will be assigned to show competence in the subject area of mathematics. Other evaluation needs are met by supplemental reporting.

If a particular content area such as algebra is divided into several levels, how should grades be assigned? Should no A's be assigned in the slower section, or should each group be considered for the full range of grades? These questions may be answered in several ways. Many would reply that all students permitted to take the course should have a reasonable chance of succeeding in it, and that there are really only two kinds of algebra: adequate fundamental algebra and honors or enriched algebra, the second being an extension of the first. Persons taking this position would expect grades to be assigned in relation to the total group and in terms of "adequate performance" in algebra. This would result in a concentration of A's and B's in the honor section and fewer high grades in the regular section.

Others would reply that the various algebra courses can be basically different, and therefore each class should be graded through the full range independently from other classes. Another argument for this approach is the motivational effect of grades. A corollary to this position is the need to describe carefully what is taught in each class so that an A in one class may be distinguished from an A in another. This may be done by attaching a descriptive sheet to the student's transcript. If such grades are used to determine senior class rank it would seem equitable to weight the honors grades so that better students will not be handicapped.

If at a particular level several independent tracks have been devised, for example, general mathematics and elementary algebra, there would seem to be every reason to grade the students in each section independently. However, the differences between the two courses should be clear to all concerned.

Although it is probably a questionable procedure at best, the arbitrary assignment of a set percentage of A's, B's, C's, D's, and F's certainly seems inappropriate for classes that have been sectioned by mathematics achievement unless classes from year to year are the same and the percentages stem from research findings. Any grading procedure that depends entirely upon other class members (ranking) may also be grossly inaccurate for small numbers.

While the above discussion does not prescribe a specific way to assign grades where several sections of a class have been set up, it does outline basic principles and problems. In summary, it suggests that the report form provide for evaluating a variety of dimensions and that the single over-all grade show the student's competence in the particular content area by comparing him with other class members and external criteria. The content of a particular class should be clearly described and included with the student's transcript if there is any question as to the nature of the class.

Interviews and Notes

An interview with parents has replaced the formal report card in some schools. In others the interview serves as a supplement to the report card. Although a good report card may provide fairly complete information, the interview adds at least two positive factors. Personal contact between parent and teacher provides a basis for mutual confidence and understanding, and the interview provides an opportunity for interaction and the asking of questions of mutual interest to parent and teacher. Most report cards have space for comment. Some schools write special notes to parents. These personal comments also may do much to clarify individual problems.

Motivation

Marks provide both positive and negative motivation for the student. The mark, however, should not be misused as a device to manipulate motivation. If it is precise and meaningful, the mark will unquestionably provide motivation. But the goal is to give an evaluation of behavior rather than to motivate. If the mark is well defined the student will understand what objectives are sought and the degree to which he is achieving these objectives. The purpose of marks, then, is clearly one of communication. The statement that "marks are undesirable because they are an end in themselves" is invalid. The task is to provide adequate marks, not to circumvent them.

Standards

The term *standard* as applied to mathematics performance suggests a degree of mathematical or arithmetical competence determined by some authority as necessary for a designated purpose or certification. A *standard* of some type is suggested as one comparison base in the discussion of reporting principles. Satisfactory completion of an algebra class may only be determined in accordance with some standard—in this case the degree of competence required. A standard is set for entrance into many college mathematics classes in the form of a certain score on a placement test.

It is apparent that a wide variety of standards is now in use. Standards are set by the individual teacher, by the school, by the employer, and by the college. Some are fixed and some are flexibly defined. There are many questions to be asked with respect to any standard. Who sets it? For what purpose is it set? How is it set? Is a particular standard logically determined, arbitrarily determined, or experimentally determined? Is it clearly defined?

It is important that normative groups and standards not be confused. All persons in a group may meet a particular arithmetical standard or none may meet it. That is, a standard may be independent of any particular group. Normative data, however, always refers to a specified group. Normative groups are helpful in determining realistic standards. The following points should be emphasized: (*a*) There are many types of standards for mathematical competence. (*b*) Standards must be clearly defined if they are to be useful, and they must be verified for some clearly stated purpose. (*c*) Rank in a specified normative group in no way suggests whether a person meets a standard unless the standard has been defined in relation to the achievement of the normative group.

Profiles

The profile, another communication device, serves one main function: It graphically illustrates a student's standing on several different tests or measures, giving an indication of relative standing and progress. It is of particular value in depicting progress regardless of the student's level of achievement, and progress is especially important in a continuing area such as arithmetic. Table 4 illustrates a profile for two groups of tests, using percentile ranks for one group and grade scores for the other, to show progress. Age scores, grade scores, standard scores, or stanines might be used instead of percentile ranks, but raw scores are not appropriate for this purpose. The profile is useful for parental conferences and it provides an overall picture of achievement for the cumulative department record.

Before drawing a profile we must ask whether or not it is appropriate and meaningful to compare or contrast the scores involved. It is necessary to know whether all of the scores in the profile are based upon comparison with the same normative group. National norms,

TABLE 4

ILLUSTRATIVE PROFILES

Hayes, Jo Ellen
_____
    Name

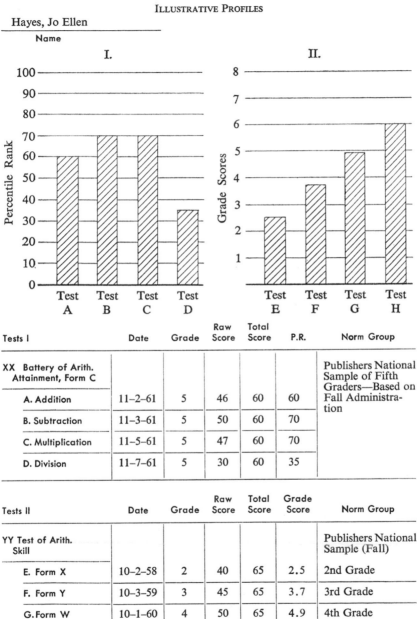

Tests I	Date	Grade	Raw Score	Total Score	P.R.	Norm Group
XX Battery of Arith. Attainment, Form C						Publishers National Sample of Fifth Graders—Based on Fall Administration
A. Addition	11–2–61	5	46	60	60	
B. Subtraction	11–3–61	5	50	60	70	
C. Multiplication	11–5–61	5	47	60	70	
D. Division	11–7–61	5	30	60	35	

Tests II	Date	Grade	Raw Score	Total Score	Grade Score	Norm Group
YY Test of Arith. Skill						Publishers National Sample (Fall)
E. Form X	10–2–58	2	40	65	2.5	2nd Grade
F. Form Y	10–3–59	3	45	65	3.7	3rd Grade
G. Form W	10–1–60	4	50	65	4.9	4th Grade
H. Form Z	10–4–61	5	54	65	6.0	5th Grade

school norms, and class norms probably should not be used as bases on the same profile unless one is attempting to compare standings on different normative groups or to relate the same score to different normative groups. If the profile is to compare facets of an individual's achievement, a common normative base for all scores is necessary. The same applies if one is attempting to show growth from one time to another. If, for example, one wishes to show growth in arithmetic skills from grade 4 to grade 5, it would be best to use the same (or equivalent) normative groups for grades 4 and 5 (except for the difference in ages). If various aspects of mathematics attainment are to be represented in a profile, the various tests should be given at the same time. If progress from year to year is to be shown, tests should be given at the same time each year.

In presenting a profile one has the common graphical problems of choice of scale and proper labeling. An improper scale may make insignificant differences appear large, or large differences appear insignificant. The profile should be self-contained; that is, all the information necessary to its interpretation should be included.

Coding and Machine Recording

Problems of recording extensive data are often solved by coding and subsequent machine operation. In coding we assign one set of symbols to another set of symbols to reduce the amount of material that needs to be recorded and/or to change the form of the material to be recorded. Sometimes coding is also used to restrict the knowledge of scores to authorized persons, but we shall not discuss this purpose.

The use of code to reduce the amount of material to be recorded may have value for classroom or cumulative record keeping in mathematics. If, for example, certain types of behavior can be classified by descriptive phrases, these phrases may be coded and more easily recorded. In a very real sense the assignment of all grades and marks is a type of coding to summarize information.

The use of electronic machines has greatly increased in recent years. The preparation or coding of data for such machines often involves a reduction in the number of symbols to be recorded and requires a change in the form of the data so that it can be accepted by the machine. In addition to electronic machines there are manual procedures that assist in sorting and counting. These include color coding, cutting of card corners, and punching of strategically placed holes in cards.

At the present time the use of electronic equipment for record keeping and reporting is usually most appropriate where large numbers of students are involved. In such cases careful planning may reduce expense and also provide additional services, particularly in maintaining continuous research. Some large high schools are now making extensive use of punched card procedures in the keeping of cumulative records, in scheduling, and in reporting grades to parents. The following procedure is being used by some schools for reporting grades. The teachers mark grades on appropriate cards. These markings permit the automatic punching of holes in the cards to record the grades. Grade reports may then be electronically printed from the cards. Electronic equipment permits rapid printing, classification, and counting as well as more complex research procedures. Computers may be programmed to do much of the basic descriptive and inferential research computation in which the mathematics teacher has an interest.

Machine procedures are more likely to be economically feasible for whole schools or cooperating schools than for individual departments. However, proper planning will involve departmental or subject matter contributions and subsequent research of specific interest to the mathematics teacher.

All that has been said about careful over-all planning, adequate choice of data, and clearly defined symbols applies to the use of machine recording. Although advance preparation for recording is always necessary, it is of special importance for machine procedures.

Summary

Day-by-day evaluation of mathematics progress and performance may be recorded in a class grade book and in a cumulative subject area folder. The folder is of particular value in maintaining a file of anecdotal comments and work samples. A cumulative summary of all basic information may be maintained on a format printed inside the folder or on a separate subject or departmental record card. A variety of information should be reported on record cards. Included are test name, form, date and grade of administration, raw scores, derived scores, and normative groups. The standard score is, perhaps, most useful for both interpretive and research purposes. The cumulative record is passed on from year to year. Department or subject area files of test distributions by class and teacher should also be maintained.

The notation used in assigning marks is arbitrary. The important factor is the meaning conveyed. The mark should relate to defined abilities, and to specific comparison groups or individuals. In addition, the mark usually conveys some value judgment as to the quality of the student's work. Thus a mark is multi-dimensional in meaning. If it also conveys a prediction concerning future success in some area, this should be stated.

Reporting and marking systems should be validated experimentally. One should determine what meanings are being conveyed to the student and the parent. If the mark is to predict future success, individuals should be followed up to determine the degree of association between marks earned and success.

No matter what type of score or mark is reported and recorded, it is essential to know the basis for comparison. In the case of test scores this means a clear definition of the normative group. It is also important that the normative group be appropriate.

Many types of scores are available to the mathematics teacher. Great care should be exercised in the selection of scores to be reported.

The profile may be particularly useful in dealing with parents and students. It provides a pictorial representation of status. In using the profile one must avoid the use of scores or results that are incompatible because of the heterogeneity of data presented.

Some large schools are now making use of electronic equipment for recording and reporting. Such equipment usually requires the use of coding procedures to reduce the amount of information to be recorded and to place the data in usable form. The use of machine procedures requires careful and extensive advance planning.

10

Overview and Practical
Interpretations

ROBERT S. FOUCH

IN THIS CHAPTER we shall discuss practical interpretations of evaluation principles, using the unifying concept of *information*. We use the information concept with the idea that all evaluation is concerned with obtaining and handling selected kinds of information about student behavior. We are concerned in this yearbook about objectives, since they function as selectors of information that is relevant in evaluation. If a curriculum includes an objective of neatness in written work, then information about students' neatness must be obtained as part of the evaluation process; if this is not a goal, then such information must be considered irrelevant. If one of the curricular objectives is the development of ability to discover in a mathematical situation, then information about students' performance in the discovery process must be obtained.

The Evaluation Process

Obtaining Information

Having decided on objectives, and thus on the kinds of information we need about behavior, we must next find or devise means for obtaining this desired information. Since a typical list of objectives usually involves many different kinds of behavior, it should be expected that many different techniques are needed to obtain appropriate information. Some of these techniques are commonplace and easy; others are unusual and difficult. Information about a child's memory of the

167

multiplication facts may be obtained by a routine paper-and-pencil test. On the other hand, obtaining information about a student's understanding of the system of decimal numeration may require the ingenious construction of items about strange, but related, systems of numeration; obtaining information about the development of certain habits may require various forms of lengthy observation, since a habit is revealed only in repeated performance of an act; obtaining information about the development of an attitude may require interview techniques or other devices; obtaining information about productive thinking may require creative activities that permit flexibility and originality.

Analyzing the Information

When this information has been obtained (that is, when the test papers have been turned in or when the anecdotal records have been written), there remains the task of analyzing and summarizing the data. The simplicity of some methods of carrying out this task frequently masks its possible complexity and causes loss of many opportunities for valuable kinds of summary information. A good example of such lost opportunities occurs when a true-false test is scored by counting the number of correct answers, and this single piece of information is used to summarize the whole test. But additional pieces of summary information are possible—among others, the number of items not attempted by the student and sub-scores on sets of related items with profiles of such scores.

Recording the Information

When evaluative information has been summarized in any fashion, it is, of course, recorded. This is standard practice and little would need to be said, except that so frequently inadequate attention is paid to the importance of securing permanence and uniformity and ready availability of recorded information. Summary information about individual students may be important for many school purposes: for example, the guidance counselor needs such information in efficient form for his work with the student; the administrator or the research worker needs such information to compare the effectiveness of two different mathematics curricula, or two different school systems, or two different methods of homogeneous grouping. The interpretation of various kinds of summary information is largely a statistical problem, and technical advice is available from a variety of sources.

Communicating the Information

Lastly, we must communicate our information. We tell parents about the progress of their children; we give information to college admissions officers, to employers, and occasionally to a variety of other agencies such as state departments of education. The task of communication is an especially difficult one, largely because the original raw information is greatly condensed and we must try to convey so much in so brief a form. As an extreme example consider the class rank at a high school graduation; a single number or pair of numbers (80 percent, or 50 out of 250) is expected to communicate something about achievement in as many as 20 courses during a whole four-year period of the life of a student. It is also of questionable validity to combine achievement in different course patterns for comparative purposes. It is almost equally difficult to condense information from a year's mathematics course into a single letter or numerical grade. With an awareness of this problem, we must either resign ourselves to the inadequate communication of a single grade or look for more elaborate ways of reporting larger amounts of summary information.

Practical Interpretations

If we are to take seriously our work in formulating objectives, then we must be sure we have objectives whose achievement we are capable of evaluating. With no evaluation there can be little or no direct knowledge as to achievement. Failure of this sort may be responsible for a host of teaching difficulties. Consider the matter of certain social applications —as a specific example, the teaching of income tax forms. The objective of this topic might be a subhead under a general objective of learning mathematics that is useful in later everyday life. The difficulty here is that any straightforward evaluation on this objective cannot be done in the school but only in the years following school; that is, a follow-up test must be used. Except in an elaborate research program, such testing is not practical. In the school situation we must resort, therefore, to immediately available means, which may be unreliable or deceptive.

Evaluating Understanding

In connection with evaluation, the statement of objectives in "behavioral form" is of the greatest importance. In evaluation we gather information about student *behavior;* therefore, in order to evaluate achievement of objectives we need to know which kinds of behavior we should observe. An especially important example, in this time of new trends and emphases in mathematics education, is any objective that refers to *understanding*. Understanding may be interpreted as a kind of behavior, but for any sort of evaluation we probably need to break this down into directly and easily observable kinds of behavior. We need to ask, for example, how we can recognize the presence or absence of understanding of the associativity of operations. How can we decide that one student has more or less understanding of this concept than another? We cannot simply ask him to state the associative property of multiplication, because we would probably be testing only rote memory. Then what can we do? There are, of course, levels of understanding of a concept to be considered. Suppose we begin by saying that understanding a concept involves the ability to apply it and that the greater the understanding, the greater the diversity of applications that can be made. As a simple example, we might ask:

By the associative property of addition,

$$(5 + m) + 3 = \underline{\quad ? \quad} .$$

At a higher level, we might ask:

If $x \oplus y = \dfrac{x + y}{2}$,

is the operation $\oplus$ associative?   Prove your answer.

At a still higher level, we would ask the student to invent operations some of which are associative and some of which are not.

The testing of understanding is an extremely difficult task and should be a challenge for every teacher and professional examiner. It is not isolated from other duties of the teacher; there is little or no difference between teaching for understanding and testing of understanding. To illustrate this point, let us ask why there is a growing tendency to teach about numeral systems to bases other than ten. Clearly it is not because we expect vast numbers of our students to use the binary system in careers as computer engineers and programmers, but because understanding of the concept of place value can produce better understanding of ordinary decimal numerals for all our students. Thus such topics are a means to an end and not the end itself. Unless this is understood by teachers, a sound idea may become perverted and we may only have bad teaching of new topics. Such a perversion would exist if base five were taught for rote memory and then tested by routine items. If base five is taught it is even doubtful that we should test at all about base five. We should test instead about base seven (or some other base that has not been studied) to find out whether some transferable understanding has been produced, or we should create ingenious questions that probe for degree of understanding of base ten. To illustrate further the interrelatedness of teaching and testing, good items for testing understanding of such a topic generally turn out to be good material for instructing in the classroom. The teacher who asks, *"Does this test item really get at understanding, or does it merely require some other type of learning?"* will probably also find himself becoming more critical, in a similar way, of classroom material. As much as we may dislike it, students will probably always study for the tests they must take; there need be nothing wrong with this if studying for the test is, in effect, synonymous with studying for our educational objectives.

Open-Book Tests

A topic that has perhaps not received enough attention is the open-book test. Several arguments may be made in favor of its use in some situations. The simplest argument is that if one is testing for understanding, there is very little that a student can obtain from referring to his text. Perhaps the open book in front of him does the student little or no good, but it is a very real pledge to him by the teacher that this is not a test of memory but rather of understanding and of ability to reason from available knowledge. Probably the first and most important effect of the open-book test is on the teacher, both in his test construction and in his teaching. Despite all the current emphasis on understanding and meaning and discovery, many mathematics teachers (including some young ones) are still in the tradition of teaching mostly for rote memory and routine manipulation of symbols. When such a teacher knows in advance that his students will have open-book tests (constructed either by himself or by others), he is motivated to teach for understanding if the test is not to be merely a measure of ability to find facts and sets of directions in the book. One can also argue that the open-book test is closer to the real situations for which people learn mathematics. Should the engineer or the mathematician know by memory a long list of integrals or trigonometric identities when tables of such information will be available to him in his real-life work? Clearly, this argument may be carried to a senseless extreme, but there is certainly some wisdom to it. Another argument is that a student will sometimes be unable to display his understanding or his ability to perform in certain ways on a closed-book test because he may be unable to recall some relevant fact. Again, wisdom must be exercised: if the intention is to test recall of an essential fact, the closed book is appropriate; if the intention is to test ability to use the fact, the open-book is appropriate; if the intention is to test both recall and use, apparently two tests are needed and they will have to be given on different days.

Are Tests Necessary?

The interrelatedness of teaching and testing leads us to a question that might have been asked at the very beginning: *Are tests really necessary in the educational process?* If we imagine a primitive educational situation such as a stone-age father teaching his son to hunt, would there be testing? In a very narrow sense, no—but in a larger sense there is certainly *performance* testing and there must be evaluation. Even this unsophisticated and untrained teacher would naturally evaluate his son's progress almost constantly in order to decide when to go on to the next step in the sequence of learnings.

A little thought will show us that what we generally mean by "testing" is really *uniform* testing of a number of students. The conscientious, skillful, perceptive mathematics teacher is constantly making evaluations of a student's verbal answers, of his blackboard work, of his facial expressions and other non-verbal behavior, but he still needs to give tests in order to have uniform and easily comparable information about the behavior of all his students in the same situation.

It has been suggested that testing might no longer be necessary with the use of teaching machines and certain kinds of automated learning programs. Is this a reasonable suggestion? In one sense it is reasonable, since the teaching machine would provide a constant, reliable record for all students working in the same situation. Analysis of the record provided by the machine would then give us the same evaluative information about each student's behavior that we ordinarily obtain by special tests, and it would give it in larger amounts. If the program material is good (that is, if it somehow matches our objectives), then we might need no further test information in the cognitive realm, but we would see with special clarity the need for other kinds of evaluation and the need for some sort of retention test to assure us that the displayed behavior of the student is more than momentary. It is almost a part of our culture for students to act as if they have the right (if not actually the duty) to forget a course as soon as the summer begins. Yet we claim that our teaching somehow prepares them for their adult lives. What is the effect of mathematics in the life of most adults? What measures do we have of how much is actually retained a year after the end of a course, or ten years after? We may claim that *something* remains over the years, but can we offer evidence? Certainly not, unless research studies are made with retention tests and we learn to construct tests to evaluate attainment of our long-range objectives.

Thinking again of our stone-age educator, we would emphasize the *number* of students. In almost any situation with a good teacher and a single student, formal tests are dispensable. When the teacher has many students the formal test is valuable as an efficient device for getting information systematically and easily. When one then jumps, in thought, to a whole nation with millions of students, the need for objective, reliable, and valid evaluation information is clear. When we consider, in addition, the tremendous geographic mobility of families in the United States, we have some sympathy for the idea that there is need for national testing programs. It is interesting to remember that the Russians, within their highly prescribed system, use oral examination to a considerable extent (our judgment is likely to be that this has several drawbacks). In the vast evaluative range from simple teacher judgment to highly mechanized use of standardized objective-type tests, there are many possible compromises and many possible combinations of techniques. It is important, however, to know what is gained and sacrificed through a given type of evaluative device or testing program.

With reference to large numbers of students, we should consider Kellogg's discussion of the use of punch cards and other, more elaborate electronic data-processing methods for obtaining greater efficiency in analyzing and using the data we have. At the present time several interesting experiments are being conducted in this connection, both by larger school districts with their own specialists and by outside companies under contract to smaller school systems. New developments in data processing may eventually be valuable to every school system.

Hartung in his chapter makes a point about students who have experiences their teachers do not want them to have. This is worth emphasis. It is not entirely a practice of the past for a teacher to assign a set of long-division problems to a mischievous student as punishment or to a good student to keep him busy. If there could be an elaborate and constant evaluation of every aspect of the learning process, the ill effects of such a practice would immediately be signalled by a drop in the student's score in attitude toward mathematics. Since we have no device for such constant evaluation data, we can only hope that teacher-awareness of what is likely to happen will have the desired effect.

Also related to the number of students being tested are Hartung's points about objectivity of scoring and choice of response technique. Indeed, since the time required to construct a good multiple-choice type test is so great, it may be suggested that the teacher with a small number of students avoid such questions, unless the situation clearly calls for them. He could, instead, devote the time to the use of a carefully prepared scoring key or set of criteria that properly allows partial credit for work correctly done on subjective items.

Item Analysis

The writing of test items is an unusually specialized form of communication in which the writer wants to convey a certain amount of information without giving more or less than he intends. To avoid wasting the student's time, the writing must be succinct and it must be very clear. This is a most difficult type of writing and the pitfalls are numerous. Even the most skilled professional item writers may sometimes produce an item that is misinterpreted by the majority of students taking the test. For published tests these may be caught in try-out forms. For the classroom teacher the best advice is that two heads are better than one. The teacher should ask a colleague to read the first version of a test and *willfully misinterpret* every item where it is even remotely possible. A little experience of this sort, although painful, will quickly show the most common difficulties of communication; more experience will eventually produce the ability to write good, precise items. When the mathematics staff is large enough to permit it, there is some advantage in having the more important tests and exams written by a committee. In addition to improvement of the writing, the discussion of which items are to be included and which are to be rejected is likely to require discussion of the objectives being tested and thus lead to better formulation of objectives.

Merwin's discussion of the information to be derived from item analysis should also be stressed. This is a very simple and very fruitful device for obtaining information that might otherwise be lost. In addition to its value in connection with improved test construction, item analysis is also a very revealing diagnostic device. For example, if the correct answer on a certain multiple-choice item is "A" but the most popular answer from a class is "D," then the teacher must ask himself, "Why did so many make this particular mistake?" The answer may be simple (insufficient time spent on the topic) or complex (a subtle misconception inadvertently created by poor textbook presentation). Frequent item analysis can turn up many interesting and important pieces of information about the instructional process; it also shows us that test papers contain a wealth of information that can be revealed by proper analytic techniques.

The discussion of illustrative test items by Sobel and Johnson suggests another value to be derived from cooperative work by two or more teachers on a test. If the writer asks someone else to name the objectives tested by each item, he may be surprised by the answers. The item written to test solution of simultaneous equations may turn out to be only a test of ability to check solutions, and the item devised for application of the Pythagorean Theorem may be answered most easily and obviously by making a crude diagram and visual estimates of lengths. This type of difficulty is especially frequent with multiple-choice items.

Integrative Items

In our proper attention to testing for objectives that are detailed and broken down into small components, we may easily lose sight of broader objectives that are, in effect, integrations of smaller learnings. The suggested reading test in Chapter 5 can be valuable in this connection. It actually tests a considerable variety of abilities, of which ability to read new mathematics is only one. It also tests the student's ability to put all his learnings together into an integrated behavior pattern. The idea of an integrative item may be extended further to the writing test or the research test. For example, the following item could be valuable with a high ability class:

The process of finding the midpoint of a line segment may be thought of as a binary operation on points (the end-points of the segment). Investigate this operation in terms of the usual properties of operations (closure and commutativity, for example). Write your results in the form of a short mathematical paper, giving appropriate proofs, counter-examples, etc. You will be graded on the number of your results and their correctness, on the quality of your proofs, and on the organization of your work.

This could be used as an open-book test, and even as a take-home test if the teacher has confidence in the integrity of his students. The reader may wish to use this item as an exercise in the task, mentioned above, of ferreting out the objectives actually tested by an item.

Interpretation of Norms

Myers' use of the phrase "comparability of scores" brings to mind a problem frequently faced by schools. Suppose that a school has regularly given a certain published arithmetic achievement test at the end of the sixth grade. Comparison of scores from year to year has provided much valuable information about efforts to improve curriculum and methods. Now the school has decided to change to another, perhaps newer, test. Even though good norms and other statistical data may be available for each test, there is some danger of destroying the continuity of records and the comparability of results. A simple solution, if sufficient testing time is available, is to give *both* tests for at least one year and thus obtain the school's own system of conversion of scores on the two tests. In this way some degree of comparability over a period of time may be maintained, and the school will keep its evaluation program up to date.

Evaluating Attitudes

The chapter by Corcoran and Gibb discusses some of the more difficult types of evaluation requiring the use of such tools as check lists, questionnaires, and observation reports. The difficulty of these evaluations, however, should not obscure their very great importance. To ignore them completely would be almost to treat students as mere learning machines, devoid of feelings and motivations and such higher, complex behavior as creativity and discovery. Much remains to be done in this area, and although most of the work may need to be done by researchers, the classroom teacher should not be discouraged from continuing such efforts. A great deal can be accomplished without special training and without special resources. Good classroom teachers have always performed this sort of evaluation, and we hope that they will continue to do so. Our major recommendation in this area is that observations be made systematically and that records be kept uniformly.

An example of a report that can be very valuable in a total evaluation program is the following teacher observation:

Johnny seems to do badly in arithmetic because he is frequently careless about his computations. Yet when he is occasionally really interested in an unusual problem, he can carry out very long computations flawlessly. Generally he seems bored in class, but once in a while I am able to produce a real sparkle in his eye. Hardly a week goes by without his bringing me some book on mathematics or science that he has found in the public library. Even though his prognostic test score looks bad and his IQ isn't high, I think he gets unusual satisfaction from mathematics and I would like to see him tried in the special advanced class.

This teacher has done an admirable job of observation and has condensed many perceptions into a valuable piece of appraisal. We ask further that he be equally perceptive about whether Suzy is careful or careless; whether Tommy is always, sometimes, or never interested; whether Bill's unique solutions are indications of creativeness; whether Mary ever reads about mathematics beyond her textbook—and that all this information be recorded so that it is easily available when it may be useful. If the value of such material is realized, the task of preparing check lists and record forms is not especially irksome or technically difficult. Suggestions for carrying out this task are found in the chapters by Kellogg and Kalin.

Reporting Practices

It is becoming increasingly imperative that grading and reporting practices be improved, especially in view of the intensity of competition for college entrance and the frequency of student transfers from one school system to another. An experienced college admissions officer may know that a B record from a certain high school indicates as much college potential as a straight A record from another school, but how can the high school in New York know the meaning of the grades of a school on the west coast from which a new student has transferred? Or in the same school, is an A in General Mathematics equal to an A in Algebra I? Is an A in geometry from Mr. Smith equal in value to an A from Mr. Brown? Is a C in the accelerated class equal to an A in the regular class? Such questions are impossible to answer except, as Kellogg indicates, by giving *more* information in report forms.

In connection with classroom grading, it is discouraging to notice that many teachers still follow the regular practice of making a test score of 70 percent or 75 percent the passing mark. There are several things wrong with this. First, the teacher cannot have any dependable information about the difficulty of the test. Myers' frequent mention of the difficulty index in the professional construction of published tests should make this clear, and Kellogg also stresses the same point. Second, if a test is constructed with such a goal, the result is likely to be a very poor spread of scores—that is, there will probably be very poor discrimination at the top levels. There is considerable merit to the maxim that a good test should be easy enough so that the weakest student gets some items right and hard enough so that the strongest student does not get everything right. In some situations the average score on a test should be in the region of 50 percent in order to get the greatest possible discrimination. There are other situations, of course, in which discrimination of rank is not the important factor. For example, if one is testing for mastery of the multiplication facts, there is no special difficulty of test construction, and one might conceivably set 95 percent as the passing mark, hoping for a very narrow distribution. The point we wish to emphasize is that setting a passing score is a complex task, and there cannot be any simple device to be used routinely.

Detrimental Effects

Evaluation, like all other human endeavors, has not been devoid of some detrimental effects. It has definitely provided a motivation and a setting for cheating. Inflexible testing programs have retarded curriculum revision by fixing course content over a considerable period of time. A teacher will frequently use precious class time to drill and coach for specific tests in order to protect his own reputation and that of the school. To such teachers the test record is more important than the achievement of broad objectives by the students. None of these misuses of tests should be permitted in the mathematics class.

Most teachers are aware of the cheating problem and meet it by close supervision, by emphasizing the importance of integrity, or by reducing the opportunities for cheating. The system reported in Kalin's chapter by Mr. Drewes of Trenton, New Jersey, may contain suggestions for many other schools, although it was not developed solely for this purpose. The device—producing many different forms of the same test— could contribute greatly in the solution of the cheating problem, a highly vexing one for many teachers.

Productive Thinking

Although we have no instruments now available to measure productive thinking in the learning of mathematics, this important aspect cannot be ignored. We may have little confidence that we can ever know how our students think, but we can observe their behavior in situations requiring thought, such as an interview, a problem-solving session, a discussion period, a student report, or the preparation of a student product. Our task consists in using ingenuity and imagination to present situations in which the student can demonstrate his originality, his creative ability, and his productive thinking.

After devising suitable situations for productive thinking, we are confronted with the problem of judging the quality of the thinking of the student. The two most common situations devised for this purpose are verbal problems and proofs of "originals." In judging the quality of solutions, we do not merely check the correctness of the answer. Instead, we focus attention on the method of solution and the thought processes involved. Is the method original and concise as well as correct? Is the solution organized, consistent, imaginative, and unusual? Has a principle, object, or concept been used in a new way? Has the solution been extended beyond the immediate and obvious? Has a diversity of possible solutions, applications, or illustrations been produced? These questions suggest the importance of originality and flexibility in a student's thinking. Such qualities of thinking should be given priority in appraising higher mental processes of our students while we wait for research to furnish us with instruments for measuring such qualities. The development of adequate instruments in this area is one of the exciting new prospects we have for the near future.

Individual Differences

A current problem of major proportions in mathematics teaching involves the provision for individual differences. Evaluation should make a major contribution in solving this problem. An adequate evaluation program should be the base on which decisions are made regarding homogeneous grouping, acceleration, advanced placement, placement in different mathematics curriculum tracks, or even placement in the proper mathematics course in college. Through appropriate evaluation we identify the gifted student, locate weaknesses, and find creative talent. To do this we need an evaluation program that includes published tests as well as teacher-made tests, observation of productive thinking as well as attitude ratings, subjective evaluation as well as objective test data. We need a way of reporting and interpreting evaluation information to the student, the parent, the teacher, the employer, and the educational institution. Such information will help build the status of education in the community and, at the same time, direct the student into activities in which he can make a maximum contribution. With the variety of appraisal instruments and methods available and the necessary financial support, we should build an improved evaluation program in every school.

A time-consuming task for most mathematics teachers is the appraisal of student products such as assignments or projects. In this regard we must recognize that assignments are ordinarily given as learning exercises rather than as evaluation activities. Our primary goal in appraising completed exercises of this kind should be to locate and correct student difficulties, not to determine a mark for a report form. However, the appraisal of a student product such as a report, project, or exhibit involves more complex factors. Here it is important to consider organization, communication skill, craftsmanship, completeness, and originality. In each case we must keep in mind the objectives to be attained by a student activity and then appraise the result in terms of these objectives.

Individualized Testing Programs

Our evaluation problems would be solved neatly if this chapter could present an ideal evaluation program in mathematics for grades 1 through 14. However, this is an impossible task. What is ideal for one school is far from ideal for another. Every system must tailor its evaluation program to its particular conditions, and the presentation of a hypothetically ideal program could be more misleading than helpful. This yearbook has presented, we believe, many valuable suggestions and the condensation of much experience; we hope it will be an aid in the solution of many practical problems that teachers face.

In conclusion, then, we urge you on to better and better evaluation and we stand by to cheer you on in the accomplishment of your task. Every mathematics teacher will need to work diligently to improve the evaluation of his students' achievement. It is a never-ending task, but a highly rewarding one in terms of satisfaction from improved instruction and increased learning of mathematics.

Annotated Bibliography Of Mathematics Tests

SHELDON S. MYERS

T HE BIBLIOGRAPHY contains an annotated listing of all available mathematics tests published since 1940 that the author was able to locate. The author will appreciate hearing directly from readers finding any errors or omissions.

Numerical references following titles refer to the Mental Measurements Yearbooks, edited by Oscar Buros and published by the Rutgers University Press (with the exception noted), and to entry numbers in these yearbooks. The books are identified by Roman numerals as follows:

I. *The Nineteen Thirty-Eight Mental Measurements Yearbook*

II. *The Nineteen Forty Mental Measurements Yearbook*

III. *The Third Mental Measurements Yearbook (1949)*

IV. *The Fourth Mental Measurements Yearbook (1953)*

V. *The Fifth Mental Measurements Yearbook (1959)*
(Published by the Gryphon Press)

Title: **Basic Skills in Arithmetic Test: III, 335.**

Publisher: Science Research Associates.

Copyright Date: 1945.

Forms: Two forms.

Grade Level: 7-12.

Content and Working Time Allotments:

68 questions, no time limit (finished in 45 minutes by half of 6th graders; finished in 40 minutes by half of 12th graders).

Type of Items and other Descriptive Information:

Free answer: Items are computation, not arithmetic reasoning problems.

Scoring and Types of Scores:

Percentiles for grades 7-12.

Statistical Information Available:

Reliabilities by Kuder-Richardson formula for grades 6-12 are .86, .96, .97, .98, .96, .97, .98.

Norms based on 3200 in 12 school systems.

Auxiliary Materials:

Diagnostic class record sheet listing 68 skills for each pupil, key, manual.

Title: **Blyth Second-Year Algebra Test:** V, 443.

Publisher: World Book Company.

Copyright Date: 1954.

Forms: A_m and B_m.

Grade Level: End of 2nd-year course in algebra.

Content and Working Time Allotments:

Fifty-five items in 45 minutes. Typical textbook items covering basic skills of a traditional course.

Type of Items and other Descriptive Information:

Five-choice objective type of item:

Fundamental operations, 18%
Operations with radicals, exponents, and logarithms, 24%
Variation, simple progressions, determinants, complex numbers, 11%
Solution of linear equations, one or two unknowns, graphic, 13%
Solution of quadratic equations, 15%
Graphical and symbolic expression; problem solving, 19%.

Scoring and Types of Scores:

Fan key or scoring stencil. Raw scores are converted to standard scores on the strip key and then to end-of-year percentile norms by a table in the manual.

Statistical Information Available:

Terman-McNemar IQs on the norms population permit taking into account the ability level of students in interpreting test results.
The manual discusses significance of score differences in conjunction with the standard error of measurement, which is 4.5 standard score points.
Split-half Spearman-Brown reliability coefficients range from .82 to .92.
Item-difficulty values for the two forms are provided.

Auxiliary Materials:

Manual, two types of keys, expectancy chart, class record sheet.

Title: **A Brief Survey Test of Arithmetic Skills,** by Arthur Traxler (Revised Edition): V, 467.

Publisher: C. A. Gregory Company (also an Educational Records Bureau edition).

Copyright Date: 1953.

Forms: A and B.

Grade Level: 7-12.

Content and Working Time Allotments:

		ITEMS	MINUTES
Part I.	Computation	40	12
Part II.	Reasoning	10	8
	TOTALS	50	20

Type of Items and other Descriptive Information:

Free answer problems. Problems cover fundamental operations with whole numbers, common fractions, and decimals. Percent is involved with some of the reasoning problems.

Scoring and Types of Scores:

Folded key provided. Score is total number right. Maximum score is 50.

Statistical Information Available:

Number of students at each grade level from 7 through 12 for the grade norms ranges from 550 to 930 for a grand total of 4,155. This population came from independent schools. Reliability as a correlation between forms A and B for 98 independent schools was .80. Other reliabilities, such as Spearman-Brown split-half, ranged from .80 to .85. One should remember that these are for a test as short as 20 minutes. Correlations with Stanford Achievement, American Council Psychological Exam, and arithmetic grades also are given.

Auxiliary Materials:

Manual, key.

Title: **California Arithmetic Test** (formerly **Progressive Arithmetic Test**): IV, 366, 411; V, 468.

Publisher: California Test Bureau.

Copyright Date: 1957 latest edition (Forms AA and BB in 1950 edition).

Forms: Five levels, two or more forms per level; W, X for lowest two levels; W, X, Y, Z for upper levels.

Grade Level: 1-14.

Content and Working Time Allotments:

Untimed.
In Battery with Reading and Language:

Test 3. Arithmetic Reasoning

Section A: Number Concept, 1-20
Section B: Symbols and Rules, 21-35
Section C: Numbers and Equations, 36-45
Section D: Problems, 46-60.

Test 4. Arithmetic Fundamentals

Section E: Addition, 61-80
Section F: Subtraction, 81-100
Section G: Multiplication, 101-120
Section H: Division, 121-140.

Type of Items and other Descriptive Information:

Five-choice objective.   Traditional arithmetic, some algebra.

Scoring and Types of Scores:

Percentile ranks for two tests and total.
Grade placement grades for two tests and total, and also mental age norms.
Hand scored with fan key.

Statistical Information Available:

Reliabilities by averaging intercorrelations of different forms: Test 3, .92; Test 4, .95; Total, .95.
More than 100,000 cases used in norming.

Auxiliary Materials:

Manual, class record sheet.

Title: **Christofferson-Guiler Analytical Survey Test in Computational Arithmetic:** V, 457.

Publisher: C. A. Gregory Company.

Copyright Date: 1957.

Forms: Two equivalent forms, 3 and 4.

Grade Level: 7-12.

Content and Working Time Allotments:

		ITEMS	MINUTES
Part I.	Operations with Whole Numbers	10	8
Part II.	Fractions and Mixed Numbers	10	8
Part III.	Decimals	10	8
Part IV.	Practical Measurements	10	8
Part V.	Percentage	10	8
	TOTALS	50	40

Type of Items and other Descriptive Information:

The items are free-answer, and working space is provided.
Items are almost entirely computational.

Scoring and Types of Scores:

The test is hand scored with alternative answers given on the key.
The scores are grade-placement for the five parts of the test and for the
the total score. Percentiles for total scores in grades 7 and 8 are
provided at the 10, 25, 50, 75 and 90 percentile levels.

Statistical Information Available:

The Spearman-Brown split-half reliability is given as .83.

Auxiliary Materials:

Class record sheet, manual, key.

Title: **Cooperative Elementary Algebra Test:** IV, 387.

Publisher: Educational Testing Service.

Copyright Date: 1950.

Forms: Equivalent forms T, Y, and Z.

Grade Level: 9

Content and Working Time Allotments:

		ITEMS	MINUTES
Part I.	Mechanics	32	20
Part II.	Graphic literal designation	16	10
Part III.	Applications	11	10
	TOTALS	59	40

Type of Items and other Descriptive Information:

Five-choice objective items.
The test goes as far as the solution of simple quadratics and the solution of two linear equations.

Scoring and Types of Scores:

Hand and machine scoring.
Percentile ranks for grade 9 for East, Middle West and West and another set for the South.

Auxiliary Materials:

Fan and stencil keys, manual for administering, class record sheets, norms.

Title: **Cooperative General Achievement Tests:** III, 316; IV, 379; V, 420.

Publisher: Educational Testing Service.

Copyright Date: 1947.

Forms: XX, Test III; YZ, Test III.

Grade Level: 13, 14.

Content and Working Time Allotments:

		ITEMS	MINUTES
Part I.	Terms and Concepts	36	15
Part II.	Comprehension and Interpretation	25	25
	TOTALS	61	40

Type of Items and other Descriptive Information:

Five-choice objective.
This a broad test over high school mathematics for the general student.

Scoring and Types of Scores:

Hand and machine scoring.
Percentile ranks for grades 12 and 13.

Auxiliary Materials:

Examiner's manual, fan and stencil keys, norms, class record form.

Title: **Cooperative General Mathematics Test for High School Classes: II, 1431.**

Publisher: Educational Testing Service.

Forms: One form, O.

Grade Level: 11, 12, 13.

Content and Working Time Allotments:

40 minutes working time.
Two-thirds of the problems deal with algebra and plane geometry; the rest cover arithmetic, trigonometry, and solid geometry.

Type of Items and other Descriptive Information:

Five-choice objective.

Scoring and Types of Scores:

Hand and machine scoring.
Percentile ranks for students with three or more years of mathematics.

Auxiliary Materials:

Manual, norms, scoring stencil, class record sheet.

Title: **Cooperative Intermediate Algebra Test:** IV, 388.

Publisher: Educational Testing Service.

Copyright Date: 1942.

Forms: Equivalent forms T, Y, Z.

Content and Working Time Allotments:

	ITEMS	MINUTES
Part I.	20	15
Part II.	12	10
Part III.	24	15
TOTALS	56	40

Content: Quadratics and beyond.

Type of Items and other Descriptive Information:

Five-choice objective.

Scoring and Types of Scoring:

Hand and machine scoring.
Percentile ranks after one and one-half and after two years of study.

Auxiliary Materials:

Fan and stencil keys, manual, norms, class record sheet.

Title: **Cooperative Mathematics Test for Grades 7, 8, and 9:** III, 305; IV, 370; V, 421,

Publisher: Educational Testing Service.

Copyright Date: 1948.

Forms: Equivalent forms X, Y.

Grade Level: 7, 8, 9.

Content and Working Time Allotments:

		ITEMS	MINUTES
Part I.	Skills	45	30
Part II.	Facts, Terms, Concepts	30	10
Part III.	Applications	30	30
Part IV.	Appreciation	25	10
	TOTALS	130	80

Type of Items and other Descriptive Information:

Five-choice objective items.

Besides ordinary arithmetic the test includes some material on geometry, algebra, business arithmetic, and graphs. Construction and use described. The test is based on 12 objectives of mathematics for grades 7, 8, and 9. These are listed with median percentages of time devoted to each by schools.

Scoring and Types of Scores:

Hand and machine scores.

Percentile ranks for each part of the test and for total score in grades 7, 8, and 9.

Statistical Information Available:

Spearman-Brown odd-even reliabilities for each part and total test (.924). Intercorrelations of the parts of the test.

Coefficients for predicting Cooperative Elementary Algebra scores.

Auxiliary Materials:

Fan and stencil keys, interpretation manual, manual for administering and scoring, norms, class record sheet.

Title: **Cooperative Plane Geometry Test:** IV, 423.

Publisher: Educational Testing Service.

Copyright Date: 1950.

Forms: Equivalent forms T, Y, and Z.

Grade Level: 10 and 11.

Content and Working Time Allotments:

		ITEMS	MINUTES
Part I.	True, sometimes true, false	30	10
Part II.	Original applications	20	15
Part III.	Deduction and proof	15	15
	TOTALS	65	40

Type of Items and other Descriptive Information:

The first 30 are "true, sometimes true, and false" items; the rest are five-choice objective items.

The test covers traditional geometry and some proof, but does not touch on coordinate geometry.

Scoring and Types of Scores:

Percentile ranks.

Auxiliary Materials:

Manual, fan key, stencil key, norms, class record sheet.

Title: **Cooperative Plane Trigonometry Test:** IV, 438.

Publisher: Educational Testing Service.

Copyright Date: 1948.

Forms: Two equivalent forms, U and Y.

Grade Level: 11, 13, 14.

Content and Working Time Allotments:

	ITEMS	MINUTES
Part I.	18	10
Part II.	12	15
Part III.	10	15
TOTALS	40	45

Type of Items and other Descriptive Information:

Items mostly deal with numerical trigonometry, trigonometry of the angle, identities. There are no items on analytical trigonometry, functions, and periodicity.

Scoring and Types of Scores:

Hand and machine scoring.
Percentile ranks for grades 11, 13, 14.

Auxiliary Materials:

Manual, fan key, stencil key, norms, class record sheet.

Title: **Cooperative Sequential Tests of Educational Progress (STEP), Mathematics: V, 438.**

Publisher: Educational Testing Service.

Copyright Date: 1956-57.

Forms: A and B on each of 4 levels.

Grade Level: Level 1: Grades 13, 14; Level 2: Grades 10, 11, 12; Level 3: Grades 7, 8, 9; Level 4: Grades 4, 5, 6.

Content and Working Time Allotments:

	ITEMS	MINUTES
Part I.	25	35
Part II.	25	35
TOTALS	50	70

Power rather than speed tests.

Type of Items and other Descriptive Information:

Four-choice objective. Items on the 4 levels are based on the following vertical mathematical threads or concepts running through the curriculum in mathematics for general education: Number and Operation, Symbolism, Measurement and Geometry, Function and Relation, Proof, Probability and Statistics.

Scoring and Types of Scores:

Scoring stencil. Raw scores are "rights only" and changed to "converted scores" by means of tables on the back of scoring keys. Percentile rank norms available for each grade level.

Statistical Information Available:

Manual for interpreting scores (1) gives percent of items in each form for each level of each of six threads listed above.

The 1958 SCAT-STEP supplement relates SCAT (School and College Ability Test) and STEP norms.

Technical Report gives reliabilities (Kuder-Richardson) ranging from .83 to .89 for the four levels.

Auxiliary Materials:

Manual for administering and scoring.
Manual for interpreting scores in mathematics.
Technical report.
1958 SCAT-STEP supplement.
SCAT and STEP student profile card.
SCAT-STEP class record sheet.

Title: **Davis Test of Functional Competence in Mathematics:** IV, 371; V, 422.

Publisher: World Book Company.

Copyright Date: 1951.

Forms: Two equivalent forms: A_m, B_m.

Grade Level: 9 through 12.

Content and Working Time Allotments:

			ITEMS	MINUTES
Part I.	Section A:	Consumer Problems	1—24	
	Section B:	Graphs and Tables	25—33	40
Part II.	Section A:	Symbolism, Equations, etc.	34—57	
	Section B:	Ratio, Tolerance, etc.	58—80	40
		TOTALS		80

The test is given in two testing periods of 40 minutes each. The manual claims that it is a power test.

Type of Items and other Descriptive Information:

All questions are five-choice objective questions.
Twelve of the questions are non-computational and require judgments.
The test is based on the objectives set forth by the Commission on Post-War Plans of the National Council of Teachers of Mathematics.

Scoring and Types of Scores:

Hand or machine score.
Percentile ranks for middle-of-year and end-of-year are provided for grades 9, 10, 11, 12.

Statistical Information Available:

Median split-half reliability is .85 for eight interform correlations.
Standard error of measurement is 5.9 for grade 9, and 4.9 for grade 12.
The Terman-McNemar IQs of the norms groups are: Grade 9, 100; Grade 10, 102; Grade 11, 103; Grade 12, 105.

Auxiliary Materials:

Each form sold in sets of 35 test booklets with Manual and Key. Separate answer sheets with class record sold in units of 35.

Title: **Functional Evaluation in Mathematics: IV, 372.**

Publisher: Educational Test Bureau.

Copyright Date: 1952.

Forms: Form A.

Grade Level: Tests 1, 2, 3: Grades 4-6; Tests 4, 5, 6: Grades 7-9.

Content and Working Time Allotments:

   25 minutes per test
   Tests 1 and 4, Quantitative
   Tests 2 and 5, Problem solving
   Tests 3 and 6, Basic computation.

Type of Items and other Descriptive Information:

   Four-choice objective.   Items exhibit a very extensive range of concepts
      and processes.

Scoring and Types of Scores:

   Separate machine answer sheets or hand scoring key.   Raw scores con-
      vertible to standard scores or percentiles by grade for each test.

Statistical Information Available:

   Norms based on about 1000 cases for each grade level for each test.
      Reliabilities are about .84 for first tests (split-halves for Test 1, and
      alternate-form reliability for Tests 2 and 3).   The corrected correla-
      tion between percentiles and teacher ratings on problem solving for
      grades 4, 5, and 6 ranged from .71 to .78.   Norms are from 16 states,
      large and small schools, and public and private schools.

Auxiliary Materials:

   Manual, key, scoring stencil, class record.

Title: **Illinois (Chicago) Algebra Test:** V, 450.

Publisher: Public School Publishing Company.

Copyright Date: 1956-58 (Formerly called Chicago Algebra Test).

Forms: One form, three tests.

Grade Level: Tests after one, one and one-half, and two semesters of algebra.

Content and Working Time Allotments:

Twenty questions in 37 minutes for each test.

Type of Items and other Descriptive Information:

Items are free-answer and cover typical verbal problems and the manipulative aspects of algebra.

Scoring and Types of Scores:

Hand scored. Each question is weighted and the total score is the sum of the weightings.
Percentile norms for each test are provided.

Statistical Information Available:

Kuder-Richardson reliabilities of .97, .94, and .96 are claimed for the three tests, respectively.

Auxiliary Materials:

Manual, analysis of errors sheet, key in manual.

Title: **Illinois (Chicago) Plane Geometry Tests: V, 491.**

Publisher: Charles H. Schutter.

Distributor: C. A. Gregory Company.

Copyright Date: 1957.

Forms: One Form.

Grade Level: Four levels: after one-half, one, one and one-half, and two semesters of high school plane geometry.

Content and Working Time Allotments:

		MINUTES
First Semester Mid-Term	Parallels, perpendiculars, angles in triangles, proof of theorem, congruence, axioms, definitions.	37
First Semester Final	The above plus circles and lines in circles.	37
Second Semester Mid-Term	The above plus secants and other lines of circle; angles formed by chords, secants, tangents; loci; ratio and proportion; similar triangles; computing altitude of equilateral triangle.	37
Second Semester Final	The above plus areas of polygons, similar and regular polygons.	37

Type of Items and other Descriptive Information:

Free answer type of item. Content of items is claimed to be common to six modern geometry textbooks, which are listed. The tests are based on very familiar and traditional textbook problems and theorems.

Scoring and Types of Scores:

Each item is weighted according to difficulty from 1 to 7. These weightings are added on the correct items to give total score. Maximum score is 100. Manual claims that a score can be considered "percent of mastery."

Statistical Information Available:

Percentile norms in manual are based on a cross section of sophomores in the Chicago school system. Norms samples for each test range from one to two thousand. Kuder-Richardson reliabilities range from .92 to .95 for the four tests. The manual gives letter grade equivalents of percentile ranks, but no basis for the equivalents is given.

Auxiliary Materials:

Manual (key in manual).

Title: **Iowa Algebra Aptitude Test** (Revised Edition): II, 1441; III, 327; IV, 393.

Publisher: Bureau of Educational Research and Service.

Copyright Date: 1942.

Forms: One form.

Grade Level: End of 8th grade or beginning of 9th.

Content and Working Time Allotments:

	ITEMS	MINUTES
Part 1. Arithmetic	30	12
Part 2. Abstract computation	25	8
Part 3. Numerical series	40	12
Part 4. Dependence and Variation	10	3
TOTALS	105	35

Type of Items and other Descriptive Information:

All items are 4-choice objective.
Development of the test is well described in the manual.

Scoring and Types of Scores:

Answers marked in test booklet which is scored with a stencil type key.

Statistical Information Available:

Validity is described in intercorrelations with algebra grades and the Columbia Research Bureau Algebra Test. The test correlates .76 with algebra achievement tests and .66 with semester grades.
The Kuder-Richardson reliability for the total test is .87.
Percentile norms for May, 8th grade, and for September, 9th grade, are provided, based on 4379 and 5786 cases respectively.

Auxiliary Materials:

Manual, scoring stencil, class record sheets.

Title: **Iowa Plane Geometry Aptitude Test** (Revised Edition): II, 1469; III, 360.

Publisher: Bureau of Educational Research and Service.

Copyright Date: 1942.

Forms: One form.

Grade Level: Before plane geometry.

Content and Working Time Allotments:

	ITEMS	MINUTES
Part 1. Reading of Geometric Content	20	10
Part 2. Algebraic Computations	20	10
Part 3. Arithmetical and Algebraic Reasoning	20	12
Part 4. Visualization	20	12
TOTALS	80	44

Type of Items and other Descriptive Information:

Four-choice objective.

Scoring and Types of Scores:

Scored with stencil key. Percentiles for raw scores on each part for boys and for girls.

Statistical Information Available:

Norms based on 1754 students. Nine tests were pretested to determine the best four for use in the final form. Validity based on 131 cases was a correlation of .705 between the aptitude test and an end-of-course achievement test. Other discrimination data are given. The reliability of the Revised Edition is .887 with a probable error of measurement of 2.72 in raw score units.

Auxiliary Materials:

Manual, scoring stencil, class record sheet.

Title: **Iowa Tests of Educational Development. Test 4, Quantitative Thinking:** III, 12; IV, 17; V, 17.

Publisher: Science Research Associates.

Copyright Date: 1951 by State University of Iowa.

Forms: X-3S, Y-3S.

Grade Level: 9-13.

Content and Working Time Allotments:

There are 53 five-choice items involving arithmetic reasoning, including simple geometry and algebra. There are one graph, several tables of data, and three geometric drawings. The questions range over most of the usual practical applications of arithmetic. 65 or 40 minutes. Test 4 is part of a 9-test battery.

Type of Items and other Descriptive Information:

Five-choice objective, one 53-item test, no sections or parts. Besides arithmetic some items extend into exponents, number series, knowledge of basic formulas. Problem settings are realistic.

Scoring and Types of Scores:

Separate IBM answer sheets. Raw scores are converted to standard scores which permit comparability of scores within the battery. The standard score scale is so designed that one standard score unit is equal to the probable error of measurement.

Statistical Information Available:

Normed on 50,000 students in 290 schools. The norms population is described in terms of comparable performance on the battery of a national stratified sample. Percentile norms for beginning-of-year and middle-of-year are available for grades 9-12.
Reliability is about .91 for pupils of the same grade.

Auxiliary Materials:

Examiner's manual, battery manual, pupil profile leaflet, profile card. Auxiliary manuals are elaborate and provide interpretive advice. Besides the examiner's manual, there are the administrator's manual, teacher's and counselor's manual, college planning manual, and a confidential summary report.

Title: **Lankton First-Year Algebra Test:** IV, 394; V, 451.

Publisher: World Book Company.

Copyright Date: 1950.

Forms: Two equivalent forms, A_m, B_m.

Grade Level: End of first year of algebra.

Content and Working Time Allotments:

55 items in 40 minutes.
Detailed outline of content provided in manual.

Type of Items and other Descriptive Information:

Five-choice objective.
Covers content of typical 9th-grade course with one item each on simultaneous linear equations and quadratics.

Scoring and Types of Scores:

Hand and machine scoring.
Percentile ranks for end-of-year norms.

Statistical Information Available:

Item difficulties in terms of mean percent pass. Split-half reliability coefficients of .84 and .87. Description of norms group in terms of Terman-McNemar IQs. Standard error of measurement is 4.8 standard score points. Norms based on 3,183 students in 57 schools in 22 states. Information on equivalence of the forms is provided.

Auxiliary Materials:

Keys, class record sheets, interpretation and administration manual, expectancy chart.

Title: **Larson-Greene Unit Tests in First-Year Algebra:** IV, 395.

Publisher: Bureau of Educational Research and Service.

Copyright Date: 1947.

Forms: X and Y.

Grade Level: First-year algebra.

Content and Working Time Allotments:

			ITEMS	MINUTES
Test I	Part 1.	Literal Notation	17	9
	Part 2.	Simple equations and formulas	17	9
	Part 3.	Simple graphs	15	8
	Part 4.	Directed numbers	27	15
Test II	Part 1.	Fundamental operations	28	18
	Part 2.	Equations of the first degree (one unknown)	25	20
Test III	Part 1.	Equations of the first degree (two unknowns)	13	18
	Part 2.	Special products and factoring	29	21
Test IV	Part 1.	Fractions	24	20
	Part 2.	Fractional equations	14	16
Test V	Part 1.	Variation	22	20
	Part 2.	Indirect measurement	18	18
Test VI	Part 1.	Powers, Roots, Radicals	28	19
	Part 2.	Quadratic equations	18	20

Scoring and Types of Scores:

Score is number right. Scoring stencil and separate answer sheets provided. Percentile norms are available for each test and also for each part.

Statistical Information Available:

Reliabilities of the six tests range from .821 to .886 for one form and .902 to .940 for the combined forms.

The probable errors of scores range from 1.98 to 2.66. The number of cases in the norms is 4324 on Form X and 4317 on Form Y. Norms are based on giving the tests immediately after completion of each unit.

Auxiliary Materials:

Manual, scoring stencil, separate answer sheet.

Title: **Lueck Algebra Readiness Test:** IV, 384.

Publisher: Public School Publishing Company.

Copyright Date: 1947.

Forms: One form.

Grade Level: Before algebra.

Content and Working Time Allotments:

	ITEMS	MINUTES
Test 1. Fundamental Operations	48	2
Test 2. Fractions	15	4
Test 3. Decimals	18	4
Test 4. Problem Solving	20	8
Test 5. General Numbers	18	8
TOTALS	119	26

Type of Items and other Descriptive Information:

Tests 1, 2, 3, 5 are free answer; Test 4 is 4-choice objective.

Scoring and Types of Scores:

Cardboard scoring key designed to line up near pupil answers. Scores are obtained by taking the number right and multiplying by some constant: Test 1 by ½, Test 5 by 2. Scores on Tests 2, 3, and 4 are number right. Percentiles are available for each test and for total score.

Statistical Information Available:

A Spearman-Brown odd-even reliability of .96 is given. The test is probably speeded, so this figure is probably high. Validity coefficients of .64 and .78 are given for samples of 126 and 112 cases.

Auxiliary Materials:

Manual, key, class record sheet.

Title: **Madden-Peak Arithmetic Computation Test:** V, 478.

Publisher: World Book Company.

Copyright Date: 1956.

Forms: Two equivalent forms: A_m, B_m.

Grade Level: 7-11.

Content and Working Time Allotments:

		ITEMS	MINUTES
Part I.	Addition and Subtraction	12	6
Part II.	Multiplication and Division	14	12
Part III.	Common Fractions	16	11
Part IV.	Decimals, Mixed Fractions, Percent	15	10
Part V.	Mental Computation and Estimation	16	10
	TOTALS	73	49

Type of Items and other Descriptive Information:

Items are all computations—there are no verbal questions. The first four parts consist of 5-choice objective questions, the fifth choice always being "Not Given"; the last part consists of 5-choice objective questions.

Front page of the test provides for the recording of subscores and the recording of more information about the pupil. All scratch work is done in the booklet.

Scoring and Types of Scores:

Scoring can be done by hand with a stencil key in three minutes or by machine.

Types of scores: percentile ranks in grades 7-11 for total score; percentile ranks in grades 7-11 for part scores.

Statistical Information Available:

Validity data is provided in the form of correlations with the Stanford Achievement Arithmetic Test for 7th and 9th graders. Split-half reliabilities are provided for total scores and subscores. Also provided are correlations with IQ and the median intercorrelations of the subscores. Tables for sex differences in the scores are provided.

Auxiliary Materials:

Scoring stencil, manual, class record sheet.

Title: **Metropolitan Achievement Tests:** I, 892; II, 1458.1; III, 345a; IV, 416.

Publisher: World Book Company.

Copyright Date: 1959.

Grade Level: 3 and 4, Elementary Arithmetic, Forms R and S; 5 and 6, Intermediate Arithmetic, Forms R, S, T; 7, 8, 9, Advanced Arithmetic, Forms R, S, T.

Content and Working Time Allotments:

	ITEMS	MINUTES
Test 6. Arithmetic Computation	45	35
Test 7. Arithmetic Problem Solving and Concepts:		
Concepts	18	10
Problem solving	30	25

Type of Items and other Descriptive Information:

The computation and problem-solving items are free answer.
The concept items are 4-choice objective.

Scoring and Types of Scores:

Raw score is the number right. This is converted to a standard score using tables in the manual. The standard score can then be interpreted by norms tables in the manual as stanines, percentile ranks, or grade equivalents.

Statistical Information Available:

The norms for the entire battery are based on over 500,000 students in 225 school systems.

Split-half reliabilities for Elementary, Intermediate and Advanced Batteries respectively are: Test 6: .92, .88, .92; Test 7: .88, .92, .91.

The standard errors of measurement are: Test 6: 1.9, 2.4, 2.3; Test 7: 2.3, 2.4, 2.4.

The school systems in the norms group are described by region and by size of community.

Auxiliary Materials:

Manual, keys, conversion table for raw to standard scores, class record sheet, class analysis chart.

Title: **Orleans Algebra Prognosis Test:** II, 1444; IV, 396.

Publisher: World Book Company.

Copyright Date: Revised edition, 1951; first edition, 1928.

Forms: One form.

Grade Level: Prior to beginning algebra.

Content and Working Time Allotments:

There are 11 tests, 9 of which are preceded by lessons. Lessons and tests are individually timed and range from 1 to 3 minutes in duration. Each lesson and test deals with an elementary aspect of algebra, such as use of exponents and positive and negative numbers. The actual working time is 39 minutes and the complete administration can be done in 45 minutes.

Type of Items and other Descriptive Information:

Items are free answer.

The manual describes how to use the test for sectioning and prediction.

Scoring and Types of Scores:

Percentile ranks are provided.

Statistical Information Available:

Norms based on 1937 beginning algebra students in six New York high schools.

Considerable validity information is provided. Correlation of the test with the Seattle Algebra Test is .60.

The corrected split-half reliability is .92. The standard error of measurement is 4.2 raw score points. The effect of speededness on reliability is not discussed.

Auxiliary Materials:

Manual, key, class record.

Title: **Orleans Geometry Prognosis Test:** II, 1471; IV, 427.

Publisher: World Book Company.

Copyright Date: Revised edition, 1950; first edition, 1929.

Forms: One form.

Grade Level: Prior to plane geometry.

Content and Working Time Allotments:

There are 9 short tests and 8 timed lessons. Total working time is 39 minutes and the complete administration can be done in 45 minutes. Each lesson and test deals with an aspect of geometry, such as reading angles, bisection, axioms, complementary and supplementary angles, geometrical problems.

Type of Items and other Descriptive Information:

Items are either free answer or matching.

Scoring and Types of Scores:

Fan key. Percentile ranks on 2899 beginning geometry students in six New York high schools, fall of 1950.

Statistical Information Available:

Validity information deals partly with original edition. Correlations of the new edition with the Seattle Plane Geometry Test range from .48 to .68. A split-half reliability of .96 was obtained with 628 students. The standard error of measurement is 3.0 raw score points.

Auxiliary Materials:

Manual, fan key, class record.

Title: **Rasmussen Trigonometry Test:** IV, 439; V, 501.

Publisher: Bureau of Educational Measurements.

Copyright Date: 1940.

Forms: A and B.

Grade Level: High school and college trigonometry classes.

Content and Working Time Allotments:

First 60 items are true-false, second 25 are 4-choice objective, last 15 are matching. Total time: 40 minutes for 100 items.

Type of Items and other Descriptive Information:

Items mostly on formal, manipulative, and numerical aspects of trigonometry, rather than analytic aspects. No items on trigonometric equations.

Scoring and Types of Scores:

Raw scores are converted to percentiles on high school or college norms.

Statistical Information Available:

Correlations between scores and term averages are .77 ± .05. Odd-even reliabilities were .87 and .90. Correlation between forms was .75. High school norms based on 472 cases and college norms on 67. Median high school raw score was 70 and college was 72. The probable error of measurement was 3.06 for high school and 2.69 for college.

Auxiliary Materials:

Manual and key.

Title: **Seattle Algebra Test:** IV, 397; V, 452.

Publisher: World Book Company.

Copyright Date: 1951.

Forms: A_m and B_m.

Grade Level: End of first half year of algebra.

Content and Working Time Allotments:

47 items in 40 minutes.

	ITEMS	% OF TEST
Part A. Vocabulary	9	19
Part B. Fundamental processes	21	45
Part C. Equations	9	19
Part D. Algebraic Representation and Problems	8	17

Type of Items and other Descriptive Information:

Five-choice objective. Parts A, B, and C are largely mechanical; Part D measures important conceptual aspects of algebra.

Scoring and Types of Scores:

Scoring stencil. Raw scores are converted on the answer sheet to standard scores. Manual provides end of first half year percentiles in terms of standard scores.

Statistical Information Available:

Corrected split-half reliability is .89. The standard error of measurement is 4 standard score points. Experimental evidence is presented in the manual as to equivalence of the two forms. The test is standardized on 8285 students in 62 schools of 27 states. The norms group is described as having a mean chronological age of 14 years 9 months and a mean Terman-McNemar IQ of 109.

Auxiliary Materials:

Manual, expectancy chart, class record.

Title: **Seattle Plane Geometry Test:** IV, 432; V, 497.

Publisher: World Book Company.

Copyright Date: 1951.

Forms: A_m and B_m.

Grade Level: End of first half year of Plane Geometry.

Content and Working Time Allotments:

There are 45 items in 4 parts. Total working time is 40 minutes. Covers following 4 areas: vocabulary, construction, computation, reasoning. Covers following three subjects: fundamental concepts, lines and rectilinear figures, the circle. "None of above" choice is used in almost all items.

Type of Items and other Descriptive Information:

Five-choice objective. Some source materials are listed but objectives are not stated.

Scoring and Types of Scores:

Scoring stencil. Raw scores are converted to standard scores on the answer sheet. End-of-first-half percentiles are provided.

Statistical Information Available:

Norms are based on 5039 students in 58 schools of 26 states.
Corrected split-half reliability is .80. The standard error of measurement is 5.5 standard score points. Information on equivalence of forms is given.

Auxiliary Materials:

Manual, expectancy chart, stencil key, class record.

Title: **Shaycoft Plane Geometry:** IV, 433; V, 498.

Publisher: World Book Company.

Copyright Date: 1950.

Forms: A_m and B_m.

Grade Level: High school geometry.

Content and Working Time Allotments:

	ITEMS	MINUTES
Part A: Concepts and facts	43	20
Part B: Application and reasoning	17	20
	—	—
TOTALS	60	40

Manual gives following relative emphasis:

1. Fundamental concepts	6– 7%
2. Lines and rectilinear figures	45–47%
3. The circle	15%
4. Proportions	22–23%
5. Area of polygons	5%
6. Regular polygons	2– 4%
7. Geometric reasoning	2%

Type of Items and other Descriptive Information:

Five-choice objective.

Scoring and Types of Scores:

Stencil key. Standard scores are obtained on the answer sheet; percentiles from the manual.

Statistical Information Available:

Corrected split-half reliability is .82. Standard error of measurement is 5 standard score points. Item difficulties are provided. Norms are based on 2914 students in 54 schools of 24 states. Mean chronological age of norms groups is 16 years 2 months, and the Terman-McNemar IQ is 110.

Equivalence of forms is described. Manual discusses uses of results.

Auxiliary Materials:

Manual, key, class record, expectancy chart.

Title: **Snader General Mathematics Test:** IV, 378; V, 439.

Publisher: World Book Company.

Copyright Date: 1950.

Forms: Two forms: A_m and B_m.

Grade Level: Grade 9.

Content and Working Time Allotments:

40 minutes for 65 items:

Arithmetic	42%
Informal geometry	23%
Graphic representation	8%
Algebra	25%
Numerical trigonometry	2%

Type of Items and other Descriptive Information:

Five-choice objective with "None of the above" as the fifth choice in most cases.

Content based on a general math course for all students where some algebra and informal geometry are included. Includes arithmetic computation, positive and negative numbers, arithmetic reasoning, graphs, mensurational geometry, ratios and map reading, similar triangles, simple algebra.

Scoring and Types of Scores:

Scoring by stencil with auxiliary answer sheet. Raw score is total number right; this is converted with a table on the answer sheet to a standard score. Standard scores can be converted to percentile scores from end-of-year norms in the manual.

Statistical Information Available:

Split-half reliability coefficient is .80 and .84 on different samples. Standard error of measurement is 4.8 standard score points.

Description of the development of the test in terms of sources and pretesting is provided. Individual item-difficulties for both forms are provided.

Norms are based on 2190 students in 35 schools of 22 states. Mean Terman-McNemar IQ is 98 for the norms group.

Equivalence of the two forms is described.

Auxiliary Materials:

Manual, scoring stencil, separate answer sheet, class record sheet.

Title: **SRA Achievement Series, Let's Figure This Out, Arithmetic:** V, 483.

Publisher: Science Research Associates.

Copyright Date: 1954-55.

Forms: Two forms, A and B, on each of three levels.

Grade Level: Grades 2-4, Primary; Grades 4-6, Elementary; Grades 6-9, Advanced.

Content and Working Time Allotments:

Grades 2-4: Writing numbers, 10 items; size, 9 items; time, 4 items; reading numbers, 12 items; number stories, 25 items; number problems, 32 items—170 minutes in 3 sessions.

Grades 4-6: Problems, 49 items; words in arithmetic, 10 items; how to read numbers, 10 items; working with numbers (computation), 44 items—120 minutes in 2 sessions.

Grades 6-9: Reasoning, 50 items; concepts, 35 items; computation, 50 items—120 minutes in 2 sessions.

Type of Items and other Descriptive Information:

Four-choice objective in upper two levels; some free answer on lower level form.

Reasoning subtests use situational approach for the items.

Scoring and Types of Scores:

Hand scoring on primary level, IBM on other two levels.

Raw scores may be converted to grade-equivalent and percentile norms by grade and by semester.

Statistical Information Available:

Reliabilities for some of subtests are: Primary computation, .54 and .64; sixth grade concepts and 8th and 9th grade computation, each .90. Nine reliabilities range from .75 to .79 and 15 range from .80 to .89. These Kuder-Richardson reliabilities are conservative. Some data on construct and predictive validities given in manual.

Auxiliary Materials:

Teacher's handbook, administrator's handbook, technical supplement.

Title: **Stanford Achievement Test:** IV, 419; V, 487.

Publisher: World Book Company.

Copyright Date: 1953.

Forms: Grades 3-4: J, K; Grades 5-6: J, K, L, M; Grades 7-9: J, K, L, M.

Grades: 3-4, Elementary; 5-6, Intermediate; 7-9, Advanced.

Content and Working Time Allotments:

	ITEMS	MINUTES
Test 1. Arithmetic Reasoning	30	35
Test 2. Arithmetic Computation	44	35

Covers traditional arithmetic.

Type of Items and other Descriptive Information:

Five-choice objective.

Scoring and Types of Scores:

Grade placement and percentiles. Scoring by stencils.

Statistical Information Available:

Grade equivalents and percentiles.
Split-half Spearman-Brown reliabilities are .896 for Test 1 and .878 for Test 2.

Auxiliary Materials:

Manual, scoring stencil, general class record, group profile chart: all batteries, cumulative pupil record card.

Addresses of Publishers

Bureau of Educational Measurements, Kansas State Teachers College, Emporia, Kansas

Bureau of Educational Research and Service, State University of Iowa, Iowa City, Iowa

California Test Bureau, 5916 Hollywood Boulevard, Los Angeles 28, California
  206 Bridge Street, New Cumberland, Pennsylvania
  110 South Dickinson, Madison 3, Wisconsin
  2114 Irving Boulevard, Dallas 7, Texas

C. A. Gregory Company, 345 Calhoun Street, Cincinnati 19, Ohio

Educational Test Bureau, Educational Publishers, Inc., 720 Washington Avenue, S.E., Minneapolis 14, Minnesota

Educational Testing Service, Cooperative Test Division, 20 Nassau Street, Princeton, New Jersey

Public School Publishing Company, 345 Calhoun Street, Cincinnati 19, Ohio

Science Research Associates, 57 West Grand Avenue, Chicago 10, Illinois

World Book Company, Yonkers-on-Hudson, New York
  6 Beacon Street, Boston 8, Massachusetts
  441 West Peachtree Street, N.E., Atlanta 8, Georgia
  2126 Prairie Avenue, Chicago 16, Illinois
  707 Bowder Street, Dallas 1, Texas
  2054 University Avenue, Berkeley 4, California